Out of the Pennines

Edited by

Bryan Chambers

Published by The Friends of Killhope.

Supported by

WEAR
VALLEY
DISTRICT COUNCIL

Front Cover: Cowgreen Mine 1950 —

from an original painting by J R Foster-Smith. The site is now beneath the waters of Cow Green Reservoir in Upper Teesdale.

Inside front and back covers: a geological map of the Rookhope Valley—

used on pages 4–5 in Sir Kingsley Dunham's article and published by permission of the Director of the British Geological Survey.

Printed by Gilpin Press, Pottery Yard, Houghton-le-Spring, Tyne & Wear.

ISBN 0 951 8939 1 2

This book is dedicated to Sir Kingsley Dunham
Founder President of the Friends of Killhope.

Out of the Pennines is the work of many people among whom are Margaret Graham and Mike Frisby who did the desk-top publishing and layout, Willie Drea who designed the cover, the committee of the Friends of Killhope who helped in numerous discussions and of course all the contributors. Bryan Chambers collected the articles and put the book together

Financial assistance was received from Don Wilcock, the W.E.A. the Countryside Commission and the Wear Valley District Council and is gratefully acknowledged. The support of our subscribers is also appreciated.

Contents

Notes on the contributors

Sir Kingsley Dunham

Director of the British Geological Survey 1966-75. His *Geology of the Northern Pennine Orefield* is the seminal work on the mines of the area. Sir Kingsley is President of the Friends of Killhope.

Tony Johnson

He began his studies of the carboniferous rocks of northern England as an undergraduate at King's College, Newcastle-upon-Tyne in 1945 and moved to the University in Durham in 1954. His research continues to this day.

Peter Wilkinson

Peter's passion for the mines and history of the North Pennines goes back more than 25 years, and he has recorded probably more than anyone else the industrial monuments of the area in that time. A founder member of NORPEX and the North Pennines Heritage Trust, Peter's knowledge is encyclopaedic.

Harold Beadle

Born into an old Teesdale family in 1909 and started work at the age of 14 years in the local quarries and barytes mines. He worked and talked with old lead miners and has spent many years researching the history of the Teesdale mines, publishing many articles and a book on the area. Harold died in the spring of 1997.

Brian Young

A geologist with the British Geological Survey and author of scientific papers on the minerals of Northern England. Since the minerals on the spoil heaps of Park Level Mine first aroused his interest in the subject over 40 years ago it is especially appropriate that he has judged the annual mineralogical exhibition at Killhope from its inception.

Brian Short

Born and raised in Nenthead. Brian's father worked at Haggs Mine while his great-grandfather was employed by the Vielle Montagne Zinc and London Lead Companies.

Bill Heyes

A keen researcher of the local history of the Durham Dales, particularly the mining history of Teesdale and Weardale. President of the Weardale Field Studies Society during 1996.

Jim Foster-Smith

Like Sir Kingsley has a lifetime's experience of the North Pennines, in his case as a mine manager and lately director of SAMUK. Now retired, he devotes much time to the South Tynedale Railway at Alston.

Charles Tanner

Met his future wife, from a well-respected Upper Weardale family, at Durham University. His curiosity about local history combined with interest in the family to produce the article in this book.

Colin Short

A Methodist minister, Colin's original enthusiasm for his native Cornwall's metal mines has transferred to our area. Researched and written a definitive work on the Brunton buddle.

Nigel Chapman

A native of Cleveland where his interest in mining began. Nigel now lives in the Midlands and is involved with the Black Country Museum and the Welsh Mines Preservation Trust.

John Pickin

A curator with the Dumfries and Galloway Museum Service, John has long been fascinated with metal mining. His particular interest is the archaeology of prehistoric mining.

Ray Fairbairn

Has been interested in the geology and mines of the North Pennines since he was a schoolboy. Now retired, he has more opportunity to continue his researches which have resulted in several articles and books on the metal mines of the area.

Rookhope in Retrospect

Sir Kingsley Dunham FRS

The valley of the Rookhope Burn, a northwestern tributary joining the River Wear at Eastgate, is the site of the earliest reference to metal mining in the Pennines in medieval records. In 1153 an iron mine and a lead mine in 'Rykhup' were granted by King Stephen to his nephew the Palatine Bishop Hugh de Puiset of Durham. Very probably the iron ore was worked from the goethite flat which outcropped at the intersection of the Boltsburn and Red veins, near the northwest end of the present village. The lead working could have been in Heights, Boltsburn, Wolfcleugh or Greencleugh veins. The Red Vein zigzags its way down the valley (Fig. 4); Greencleugh Vein is a western branch of it. The Romans were here, for they left behind an altar to Silvanus, a model of which can be seen in Eastgate village, but there is no evidence that they worked underground. Elsewhere, they mined extensively in the Mendips and employed water-wheels underground at their Spanish mines.

I first became acquainted with Rookhope mining in 1929 when, as an undergraduate, I accompanied Professor Arthur Holmes and Dr. William Hopkins on a visit to Boltsburn Mine, arranged to show a distinguished visitor, Professor Reinhart from Basel what exciting minerals we had in Durham. Tom Maddison the manager, received us; we were given acetylene lamps and we descended the shaft noting the water-wheel which was driving the pumps (Fig. 1). On Watts' Level we climbed into mine cars and, pulled by a battery electric loco we travelled nearly two miles to No. 3 Underground Shaft where we descended 138 feet to the bottom working level of the mine. Here we saw the vein, only about three feet wide but passing through a crosscut in altered limestone we came to the workings in the replacement flats for which this mine was famous. Fluorite, galena, quartz and siderite had taken the place of the limestone and where there were extensive open cavities a wonderful show of crystal faces of all these minerals was displayed.

In addition to the big water-wheel another feature of the industrial archaeology was still intact at that time. This was the smelt mill, beyond the west end of the village. The hearth was still intact and an arch carried the great stone-built flue over the road and up the valley side for nearly a mile. This mill had been in use until 1919, the last of the traditional mills to operate. At the time of our visit the concentrates from the conventional dressing plant, containing crushers, jigs and tables, were sent to Walker Harkers in Newcastle for smelting. A few years afterwards the arch was removed and the damaged mill gradually collapsed. A party of do-gooders from Newcastle eventually cleared the site.

In 1930 my first degree completed, I was awarded a Senior Exhibition for industrial research by the County Council, worth £180 per year, or in real terms 1995, £4,500. My chosen subject was the origin of the Pb Zn Fba deposits of the North Pennines. It had been the custom of the Weardale Lead Co. to receive mining students from Armstrong College for their practice period and the company agreed to take me on for a similar apprenticeship. I already had the advantage of knowing the

Managing Director, Henry S. Willis, through my family; he had been the London Lead Company's last manager when it closed its operations in Teesdale in 1906. Later I also met his fellow directors, Anthony Wilson of Keswick and E Deas of Cameron Swans Newcastle. J. Alvan Hill, the company's surveyor, both well-informed and helpful, became a life-long friend; his beautiful plans are now in the county archive. My grant enabled me to buy a very second-hand, bull-nosed Morris Cowley two-seater which gave me freedom to travel all over the research area. I began work at Boltsburn Mine in September, going in with the 6.30 a.m. shift and learning the rudiments of mining technique as well as spending time recording in great detail the geology. At 8.30 in the morning we sat down to eat our bait (generally a tea-cake with jam) and one morning I noticed one of the friendly miners taking a tin and collecting water running down the galena in the working to drink. 'Are you not afraid of lead poisoning?' I said; 'Not at all', he replied, 'I've done this man and boy for 40 years or so!' Unoxidised galena is evidently not much soluble in water! The miners worked on a bargain system of long standing, in partnerships; often the workings were known after the leader of the group. Thus, Watt's Level, Philipson's Sump, Hogarth's Rise have given some of them a certain immortality on the beautiful plans kept by the Beaumonts and their successors The Weardale Lead Company. Traditionally, the lead miners of Weardale were also smallholders, and Boltsburn Mine still ceased work for the harvest.

My conclusions about Boltsburn may be summarised briefly:

(i)   The vein, a minor fault, running ENE carries orebodies in the Coal Sills, Sandstone, and Little Limestone as well as the Great Limestone for the first mile; the flats first appeared at 4,780 feet and were still continuing at the eastern forehead of the bottom level 11,652 feet or 2.25 miles from Boltsburn shaft;

(ii)   The flats appeared where flow was restricted above the Great Limestone by the appearance of impermeable Shale;

(iii)   In both vein and flats deposition of single phases appears to have been the rule, but I was unable to establish a general sequence of such phases;

(iv)   To a remarkable degree therefore the mineralisation followed the Great Limestone as it dipped NE at 1 in 45 (2 degrees);

(v)   Figures later supplied by the company showed that for the period 1901, when the flats were discovered to 1932, the average recovery per ton of ore mined was 17.3 per cent PbS; between 1901 and 1916 the range was from 22.2 to 18.5 per cent whereas from 1921 to 1932 the range was 16.2 to 10.9 per cent; nevertheless I can testify that the easternmost headings in the flats were still in high-grade ore.

I began to enjoy underground work and comradeship and from Rookhope my activities spread to Nenthead, where Amos Treloar was managing for the Vieille Montagne Zinc Company, with Percy Blight as surveyor; and to Hunstanworth where

2

Fig. 1 Boltsburn shaft and water-wheel in 1931.

Photograph, Sir Kingsley Dunham

Christopher Heeps was running the mines owned by the Joicey family. From these active operations I went on to visit every old mine that could be entered and to examine every opencut and waste heap in the 1,500 sq km of the orefield, and my Ph.D. thesis submitted at the end of 1932 was the outcome of these observations, coupled with laboratory work at Durham and, under Dr Johnny Smythe, in the Metallurgy Department at Armstrong College. At this stage the results included an assessment of the broad and local structural problems and a demonstration of a broad regional mineral zoning.

At the south-east end of Rookhope village, the Red Vein turns from NNW to run due east along Stotfield Burn. In 1931 the Weardale Company were reopening the Low Shaft of the old mine, previously operated for lead during the nineteenth century to search for fluorspar. They had pioneered the use of the mineral and had shared in a market for the steel-making industry. Here I was able to see the Red Vein 10 to 12 feet wide of fluorite, quartz, siderite, and calcite which had been slit to take out the galena. Stotfield Burn mine proved to be a very successful source of spar and was in work until 1970.

When I published my results on the Northern Pennines in 1934 I suggested that a concealed granite intrusion beneath the orefield might have supplied the necessary mineralising fluids. I had in the meantime been elected to a Commonwealth Fund Fellowship at Harvard University where I was able to carry on my researches. The notion that granitic magmas upon crystallising provided residual fluids containing metals had achieved a dominant position in America thanks particularly to Waldemar Lindgren and his associates, like L. C. Graton at the US Geological Survey. These men were now respectively professors at Massachusetts Institute of Technology and Harvard and I was able to study with both of them and to take on a research project in New Mexico to investigate the granitic intrusions in the Oregon Mountains and the metalliferous deposits fringing them. When I published my Bulletin on this work in 1936 I followed the American Alpha but not without some questioning; for example the pegmatites, where the metal-bearing fluids ought to have accumulated, showed no evidence of this and late NS faults associated with the basin/range structure were in places highly mineralised. But that there was some connection between granite and ore-genesis I had no doubt.

When therefore I was sent back to the Northern Pennines as an officer of the Geological Survey in 1939, the possibility of underlying granite was still in my mind; but I had no means of following it up and my three years in the field were devoted to amassing the full detail of the mining situation and to encouraging production, particularly of fluorspar, and later of zinc ore, at the mines on behalf of the Non-Ferrous Minerals Control of the Ministry of Supply, both these being essential for the war effort. Here I was closely associated with the Control's mining engineer James Jackson, a cheery Lowland Scot recently returned from managing the copper mine at Tetiuhe, near Vladivostock, for Selection Trust Ltd. The details amassed, formed the basis for my 1949 Memoir.

In Rookhope during the war period the Groverake Mine at the head of the valley was taken over by Blanchland Fluor Mines on behalf of Scottish steel-maker, McKechnies, so that mining activity in the valley now included two important spar mines. This was just as well since, very sadly Boltsburn East Lead Mine had been closed in 1932, not for lack of ore, but because of the very low prevailing price of lead. The water-wheel-driven pumps at Boltsburn shaft were kept running but it did not prove practical to reopen the mine either during or after the Second War, and they were finally dismantled in 1950. In 1946 I became Head of the Petrographical Department of the Geological Survey and this enabled me to return to some problems of the mineralogy of the Pennine deposits, particularly to the identification of the carbonates in the altered limestone between the vein and the flats at Boltsburn. These proved to be a mixture of anchorite, the dolomite-ferrodolomite series, and siderite. It was now possible to explain the oxidation of these materials to form the Bilbal-type iron ores like those from the Great Limestone flats at Rookhope and those adjacent to the Burtree Pasture, Groverake and Greencleugh Veins at the head of the valley. The later three deposits were replacements of the Lower Felltop Limestone and at a rough estimate they must have yielded over 500,000 tons of iron ore, the transport of which was made possible by the remarkable railway, constructed by the Weardale Iron Company during the latter half of the nineteenth century, that ran round the high fell from Weather Hill above Crawleyside to Consett to link with Rookhope by means of an incline driven from a stationary engine at Bolts Law. A subsidiary line followed the top of the Great Limestone outcrop from Rookhope round to the main dale and to the north-west it made Groverake accessible via Rispey (the only mine where primary siderite was worked) and Wolfcleugh. These lines had been abandoned after the Great War but the LNER incline from Weather Hill down to Stanhope was still functioning in my early days.

My return to Durham in 1950 as Professor of Geology soon led to re-establishment of relations with the Weardale Company, to which I became geological consultant. Mr Willis had retired, and Mr Hill had resigned to become manager of the Closehouse barytes mine in Lunedale. William Wardrop who had come from Falconbridge, Ontario, to succeed Alvan Hill in Allendale, now became general manager and moved to Boltsburn House, Rookhope. The development at Stotfield Burn came to fruition under him. By 1957 the eastern end of this section of the Red Vein had been reached and the vein had turned away towards the ESE and become barren as it headed for the tunnel, also driven in barren ground, from Stanhopeburn Mine. A second mining engineer Henry Green joined the company, and ultimately succeeded William.

Among my earlier visitors at Durham were two research students from Cambridge, Martin Bott and David Masson-Smith, who invited my opinion as to the merits of a gravity study of the Alston Block. The idea was very welcome since it might provide real evidence for my concealed granite. Their results were more valuable than I dared hope, for they showed an elongated central area of gravity deficiency (or a Bouger Anomaly) that could be best explained by the contrast in density between a lighter granite pluton and the heavier rocks into which it was intruded. We now had a basis for raising funds to test this concept by drilling. It happened that the distinguished physicist Professor Patrick Blackett was urging

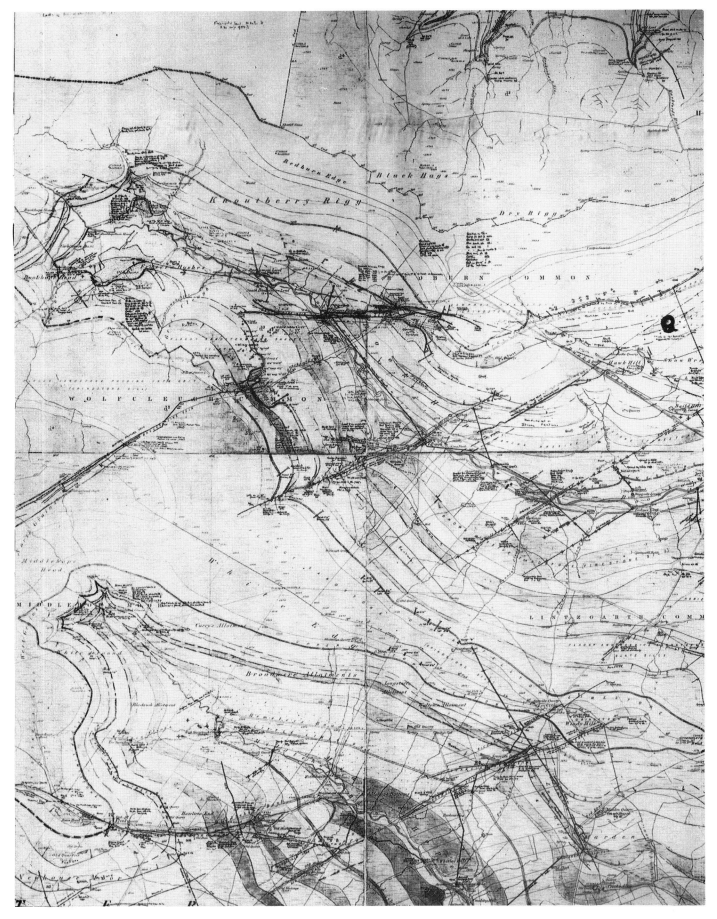

Fig. 2. Geological map of the Rookhope Valley as at 1939–40 representing the end of the lead-producing period.

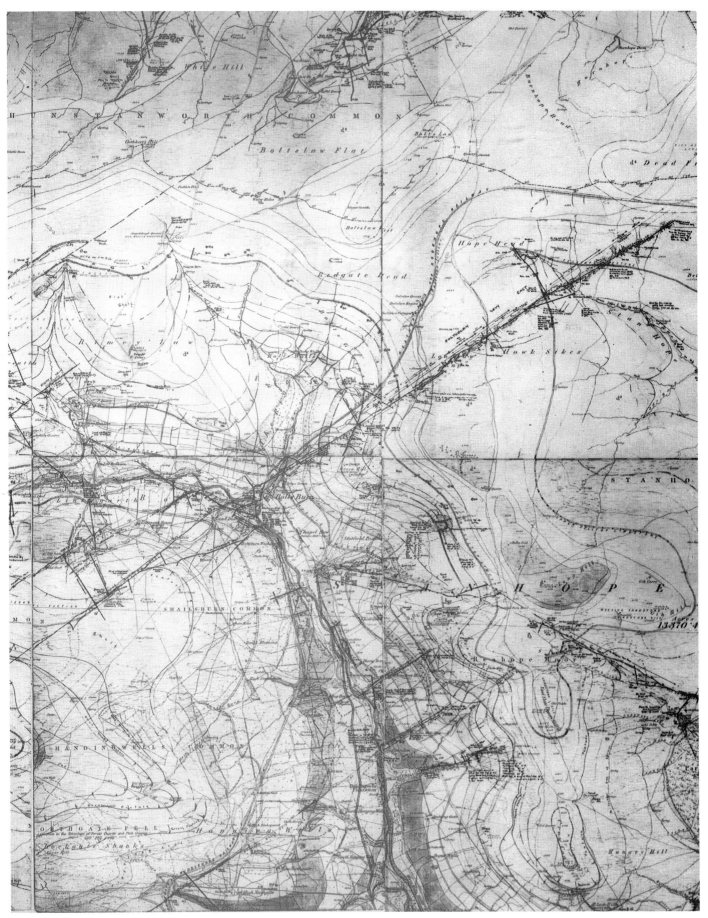

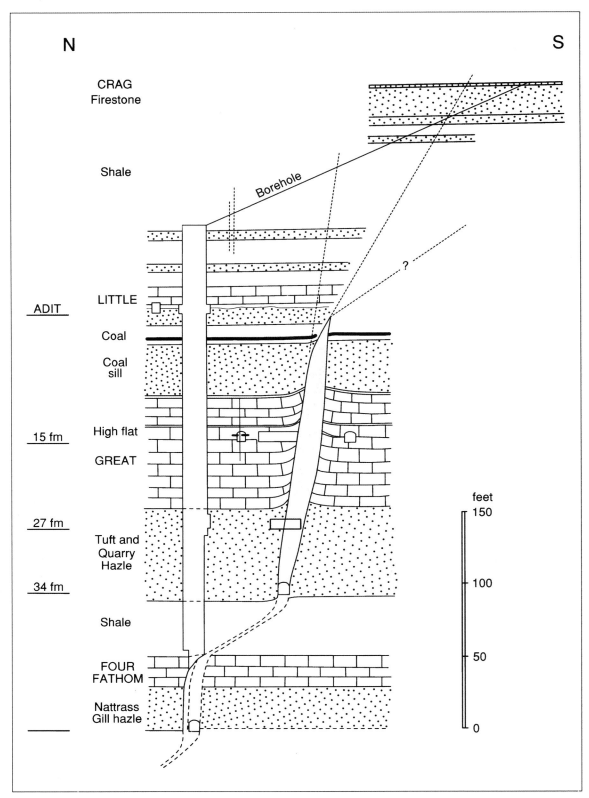

N

S

CRAG
Firestone

Shale

Borehole

?

ADIT

LITTLE

Coal

Coal
sill

15 fm

High flat

GREAT

27 fm

Tuft and
Quarry
Hazle

34 fm

Shale

FOUR
FATHOM

Nattrass
Gill hazle

feet
150

100

50

0

Fig. 3. Section at No. 4 underground shaft Stotfield Burn Mine. Reproduced by permission of the Institution of Mining and Metallurgy from *The future of non-ferrous mining in Great Britain and Ireland.*

the government of the day to fund some major scientific projects in a way similar to what was happening both in the USA and USSR; and the Wilson Government had just agreed to make money available. Through the Department of Scientific and Industrial Research I was offered £35,000 to drill, to test the granite hypothesis. The chosen site was the mine yard at Rookhope, because this was directly over the eastern cupola of the supposed granite, with Boltsburn and Red Veins dipping towards it. The drilling was undertaken in 1960 by the Foraky Company from Nottingham and a rig adequate to go to a mile deep if necessary was erected (Fig. 5). Boring commenced at 11 inches diameter and was gradually reduced

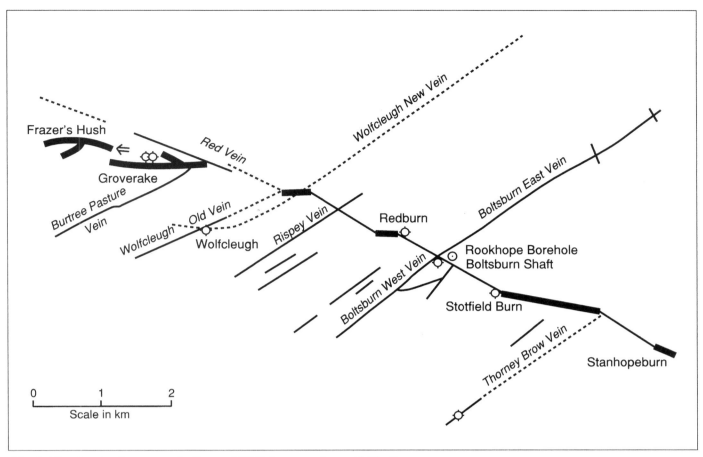

Fig. 4. Map showing fluorspar orebodies as at 1990, for comparison with Fig. 2.

to 6 inches before the hole was completed. As the intention was to gain the maximum scientific advantage from the project the hole was fully cored. One of my research students Brian Hodge was employed as research assistant to supervise the boring and to log the cores as they came out. I calculate that Brian must have moved over 35 tons of core to the old miners' hall, which we had taken over as a core house, where they were placed on steel racks. One day in February 1961 I had spent the morning in Stotfield mine and had joined Brian to look at the first core for that day as it came from the borehole. The great moment had arrived for instead of Carboniferous sedimentary rocks, the hole had now entered a foliated igneous or perhaps metamorphic rock, at 1,281 feet depth, with a strong micro foliation at right angles to the core. Drilling was continued in granite to 1,750 feet. It was quite clear from the cores immediately above the granite that these were of unmetamorphosed sediments, resting on an eroded surface. Age-determination on the granite by Dr Morebath at Oxford and Dr Miller at Cambridge gave a figure of 360 million years showing that we were dealing with a late Devonian intrusion. Clearly it could not have supplied from its residual juices the hydrothermal fluids that mineralised the overlying sediments.

Laboratory work commenced forthwith; indeed at an early stage we had installed a 24 inch diameter diamond saw at the core house and had cut a segment from each core for transport to the Durham laboratories. When the hole was complete Dr Hodge left for an appointment with La Port Industries in Derbyshire and was succeeded by two new research assistants,

Ansel Dunham, fresh from his D.Phil. at Oxford and Maureen Kaye from the University of Canberra. Fig. 6. is a reproduction of the log of the bore hole. Altogether 17 mineralised intersections were found; one, with an adjacent small fold was fairly certainly the Red Vein but the only one having immediate mining promise was that in the Jew Limestone where strong fluorite and zinc mineralisation appeared. At a later stage with the collaboration of the Canadian company Cominco further borings were made to test the extent of this mineralisation but the results were unfortunately not encouraging enough to justify the very deep sinking involved. Both veins however were still live in the granite.

After the borehole had been completed it was used for two important sets of geophysical observations, in addition to the geophysical logs that were made while it was in progress. Systematic measurements of temperature showed after stability had been reached that the water at the bottom of the hole was at 94.2 °C, or hotter than a hot bath. Secondly the hole was used to house a vertical seismometer which Dr Roger Long employed in connection with two horizontal arrays at right angles to carry on research in three dimensions on incoming signals from earthquakes and, in at least one instance on a nuclear test, probably Russian. Before leaving the Geological Survey in 1975 I had initiated, by means of a report to the Rt. Hon. Wedgewood Benn, Minister of Energy, a programme of research into the possibility of making practical use of the heat in the earth's crust. By the 1980s this programme had progressed far enough for the possibility of drilling the

Fig. 5. Rookhope Borehole, the rig in 1960.   *Photograph: B. L. Hodge*

fine wide vein of spar. This seemed to have come in not only where the EW direction was resumed but where a small ENE vein called Straightlegs had cut through. Development during the next five years revealed two major ore bodies with widths of spar exceeding 12 feet and against a range of strata from the high Namurian sandstones down to the Three Yard Limestone. By this time the ownership of the Weardale Company had passed to Imperial Chemical Industries Limited. This might be said to have resulted from the installation of facilities for sink-and-float and for flotation at the Rookhope Treatment Plant; ICI was the principal customer for the nearly pure CaF_2 the production of which had now been made possible. Also about this time F. W. ('Rick') Smith came to Rookhope as a research student from Durham to investigate the geochemistry particularly yttrium content of the fluorspar. After completing his Ph.D. he joined the company as resident geologist and was responsible for later stages of development and drilling at the now very successful Red Burn mine.

Meanwhile other important changes of ownership in Rookhope had been taking place. In 1969 the steel industry had been nationalised with the formation of the British Steel Corporation, which now took over Groverake mine. Here a more vigorous mining policy was pursued by improving the main shafts. The ore was taken to Hunstanworth for milling. Then in 1977, ICI disposed of the Weardale Lead Company to Swiss Aluminium (UK) Ltd, a company that had been prospecting the Teesdale Mineral Belt from Bollihope under the management of Jim Foster-Smith. They were also enabled to take over Groverake from BSC and there was therefore potential for a more substantial output of crude fluorspar under a single company than hitherto. Their operations saw the completion of extraction at Red Burn and as they began to have doubts about the future of Groverake they commenced a drilling programme at Fraser's Hush. The immediate problem however was to find sufficient capacity to deal with the remaining crude fluorspar and they therefore erected, in an old quarry at Frosterley, a fine new flotation mill. The Rookhope mill at the best had capacity for 120 tons per day; the new one was designed for 250. It was opened on 14th November 1978 and is still working.

In 1984 the market for high-grade fluorspar deteriorated considerably and at the same time BSC decided to reduce its operations and to dispose of its Pennine mines. SAMUK, at the same time decided to withdraw from the field and a serious crisis for Rookhope and Weardale in general was unfortunately

Rookhope borehole to greater depths to be considered. In the mean time however vandals had broken into the shed over the borehole, removed the capping and dropped steel objects down the hole which made it impossible to resume the drilling. Rookhope might otherwise have become the site of a geothermal test with significant practical implications for the future.

Returning now to the mining situation, in an article in the Institution of Mining and Metallurgy study of *The Future of Non-Ferrous Mining in Great Britain and Ireland* 1959 I had suggested that there was ample space between the village and Groverake for one or two EW productive stretches of the Red Vein to exists, even though it had turned to its unproductive direction at the east end of the Groverake workings. As Stotfield Burn mine approached the exhaustion of its substantial ore bodies in 1964 attention was given to this possibility. A low water level in the beck had showed a quantity of fluorite close to where Redburn joins it and on this Harry Green commenced the sinking which by 1965 had revealed a in prospect. A solution came from an unexpected quarter. At Bakewell in Derbyshire a new mining company Minworth Ltd. had been started by Peter Mason and Dr Joe Mason, two unrelated gentlemen, one an entrepreneur the other an experienced geologist. Minworth raised sufficient capital to take over the SAMUK interests and a subsidiary called Weardale Minerals Ltd., and to acquire the BSC interests as Weardale Mining and Processing Ltd. My friend of long standing Sir Peter Kent, formerly Chief Geologist and later Exploration Manager of British Petroleum Ltd. became Chairman of Minworth and to give what help I could, I joined as non-executive director of the Weardale Companies. Groverake with its exceptionally wide orebody, up to twenty feet in places, extending from the Lower Felltop Limestone down to the Three Yard Limestone continued to prosper but it was clear that unless further reserves could be discovered in depth, or laterally the end was in sight. In depth a bore hole from the bottom of the mine proved the Whin Sill in the Lower Little Limestone position and the possibility remained that this thick rigid formation might be a bearing horizon. This has not however been proved either, here or anywhere else along the Red Vein.

The Sill does carry large fluorspar bodies at Blackdene North and Cambokeels Mines on the Slitt Vein. Latterly the successful borings at Fraser's Hush were followed up by driving the 80-fathom level westwards from Groverake shaft to cut Greencleugh vein which proved to be satisfactorily productive before Fraser's Hush was reached. Here, then, Weardale Minerals Ltd. had very promising new resources in sight. In the meantime that company, or rather its parent Minworth concern, had invested heavily in the principal fluorspar mining area Laurentia in eastern Canada. Most unfortunately the market for high quality fluorspar in America was ruined by the importation from China of an equally good product at less than three quarters of the market price. Laurentia went into liquidation, dragging with it Minworth's other subsidiaries in Weardale and in Scotland.

This disaster for Rookhope was not, however, to be the end of mining in the valley. For the Sherburn Sand Company stepped in and took over the Fraser's Hush operation and the Frosterley Mill and both are continuing to operate.

Let us look back over the contributions that Rookhope had made to mineral production during its history. The earliest interest that of the Bishops of Durham was to win silver for their coinage (which they issued from the twelfth to the sixteenth century), for lead for roofing churches and for iron ore. We have no figures for the quantities involved. In the seventeenth century the Beaumonts of Allendale acquired the Weardale lease and the following incomplete figures for the W. B. Company are available:

Mine	Date	Prodn. of Pb Concentrate
Wolfcleugh	1818–1847	325 tons
Boltsburn	1818–1876	23,726 tons
Groverake	1828–1876	4,644 tons

Almost certainly there would be lead produced by the W. B. Co. during the eighteenth century but separate figures are not available. Under the Weardale Lead Co. the following figures are available:

Mine	Date	Prodn. of Pb Concentrates
Boltsburn Vein	1884–1900	11,831 tons
Flats	1901–1931	89,320 tons
Vein	1932–1940	2,738 tons
		West Level

Total recorded lead production 132,584 tons from which at least 1.5 tons of silver and at least 100,000 tons of lead metal. To this must be added output prior to 1818 and recovery from fluorspar mining. The totals for fluorspar up to 1940 were:

Mine	Date	Prodn. of Fluorspar
Boltsburn	1901–1931	7,299 tons
Groverake	1901–1940	31,817 tons
Stotfield	1905–1940	15,168 tons

From 1940 on production of fluorspar in Weardale greatly increased and the totals, in thousands of tons of crude spar for the several mines are as follows:

Groverake	674
Boltsburn	92
Redburn	328
Stotfield	315
grand total	1,410 thousand tons

Now looking back on Rookhope, the valley acted as a focus and challenge at the start of my researches into ore-genesis, and sixty five years later these remain a major interest. My first results (1934) showed that a broad lateral mineral zonation had been imposed on an elaborate geometrical pattern of ENE, NNW veins and the zigzag visectrix of these directions, cutting the Alston half-dome. Temperature control of hydrothermal solutions was postulated, and was later justified by the work of Sam Sawkins, Roy Phillips and Rick Smith on homogenisation of fluid inclusions in quartz, fluorite and sphalerite. The existence of a few places where an early high-temperature quartz-chalcopyrite-pyrrhotite phase was to be found indicated where the solutions rose from depth before spreading into lateral tabular openings afforded by the junctions of ENE and EW veins with selected hard wall rocks. At least one such centre lies beneath Rookhope. The gravimetric evidence provided by Martin Bott and David Masson-Smith clearly showed that concealed granite underlies these centres; but the evidence of the borehole and of the dating of the Weardale Granite at 360 million years by Miller at Cambridge and Morebath at Oxford strongly indicates that the solutions were not the hydrothermal residua of this granite. This conclusion challenged not only my own early ideas, but also a widely-held international concept. Rookhope has long been known in museums around the world for the beautiful mauve fluorspar crystals from Boltsburn, but it has now emerged in scientific circles. This has resulted from an invitation to me to give the first Distinguished Research Lecture of the Society of Economic Geologists at its meeting at Dallas, Texas in 1963; at this time I also spoke at USGS Washington, Denver, and Menelo Park (California), and also Yale, Harvard and Austin (Texas) Universities. Later on, the project was also described in Moscow, Leningrad, Novosibirsk, Kiev and Tbilisi, and also Kyoto, Seoul, Sydney and Perth. I have been very fortunate in attracting distinguished collaborators in these genetic studies. The liberation of huge quantities of Fe and Mg by the conversion of Whin dolerite into 'White Whin' adjacent to the veins was established by Lawrence Wager, John Smythe and Dick Ineson, thus revealing the source of the iron carbonates

Quart. J. geol. Soc. Lond. vol. 121, 1965 (*to face p.* 414)

PLATE

ROOKHOPE BOREHOLE

UNIVERSITY OF DURHAM & D.S.I.R.

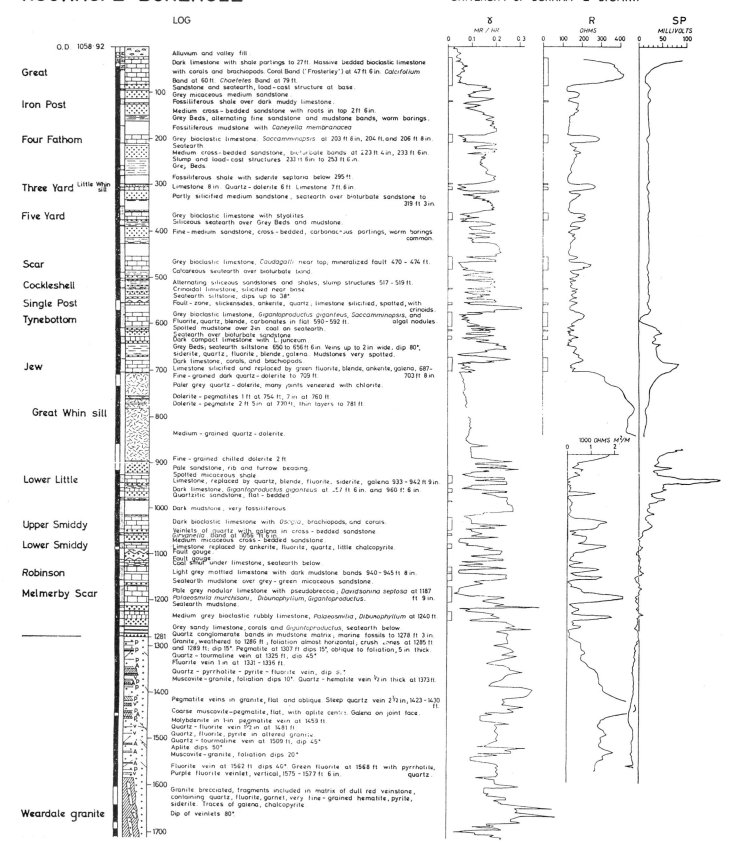

Fig. 6. Log of the Rookhope Borehole,

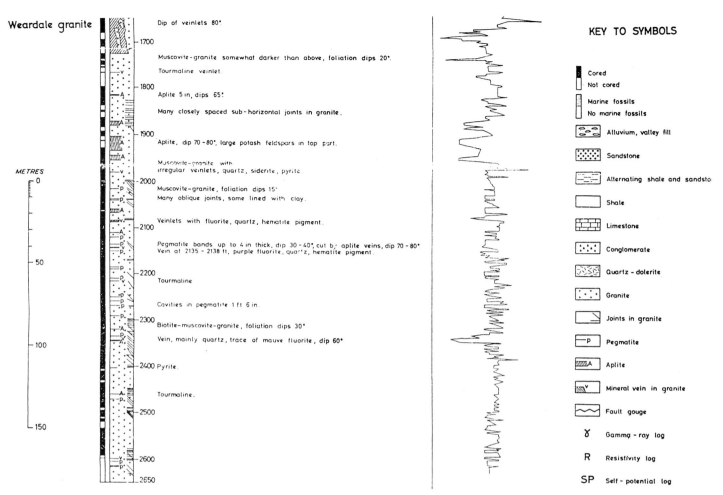

Weardale granite

KEY TO SYMBOLS

Dip of veinlets 80°
— 1700

Muscovite-granite somewhat darker than above, foliation dips 20°.
Tourmaline veinlet.
— 1800
Aplite 5 in, dips 65°.
Many closely spaced sub-horizontal joints in granite.
— 1900
Aplite, dip 70-80°, large potash feldspars in top part.
Muscovite-granite with
irregular veinlets, quartz, siderite, pyrite.
— 2000
Muscovite-granite, foliation dips 15°
Many oblique joints, some lined with clay.
Veinlets with fluorite, quartz, hematite pigment.
— 2100
Pegmatite bands up to 4 in thick, dip 30-40°, cut by aplite veins, dip 70-80°
Vein at 2135-2138 ft, purple fluorite, quartz, hematite pigment.
— 2200
Tourmaline
Cavities in pegmatite 1 ft 6 in.
— 2300
Biotite-muscovite-granite, foliation dips 30°
Vein, mainly quartz, trace of mauve fluorite, dip 60°
— 2400 Pyrite.
Tourmaline.
— 2500
— 2600
— 2650

METRES
0
50
100
150

■	Cored
□	Not cored
	Marine fossils
	No marine fossils
	Alluvium, valley fill
	Sandstone
	Alternating shale and sandstone
	Shale
	Limestone
	Conglomerate
	Quartz - dolerite
	Granite
	Joints in granite
=P	Pegmatite
A	Aplite
v	Mineral vein in granite
	Fault gouge
γ	Gamma - ray log
R	Resistivity log
SP	Self - potential log

Diagrammatic log of the Rookhope borehole: radiometric (gamma-ray), resistivity, and self-potential logs are shown.

and resulting ore deposits. Studies of stable isotopes in the sulphides, undertaken with Mike Solomon and Athol Rafter indicate a Carboniferous rather than Permian source for the salts in the hypersaline formation waters that became the mineralisers. Solomon also showed that barium was present in these as they passed through the fluorine zone, even though barite and witherite were not deposited in this zone. The most reliable age for the mineralisation was obtained by Stanley Bowie on uraninite from the supposed Boltsburn vein in the Weardale granite; the figure was 282 million years. There may have been some later phases also. Brian Young, also of the British Geological Survey surprised us all by discovering migmatite intergrown with Pennine sulphides suggesting that the Whin Sill, intruded at 292 my, may still have been hot when the minerals were formed. The borehole provided Tony Johnson with a complete section through the Brigantian and Aspian divisions of the local Carboniferous, and he is just completing a major work on the evolution of the fossil faunas. I am particularly grateful to him for being responsible for the Rookhope cores during the years and for making it possible for a very large number of potential and actual geologists to see these, and where appropriate to take samples.

In my view good economic and industrial geology requires excellent fundamental research behind it. I think it can be plain that here, the research led to the discovery of new major orebodies at Redburn and Fraser's Hush in Rookhope, as well as others beneath Blackdene, Cambokeels, Closehouse, Silverband, and also an extension in depth at Settlingstones.

In Durham, sadly we have been saying farewell to a great coal mining industry which has reached the end of its economic viability. This is not yet the case in Rookhope.

The cold figures quoted above represent a massive record of human toil and enterprise, the scale of which reached its maximum during the first thirty years of the century and the 1970s. The resources in sight, though by no means negligible, can only have a limited life. The main hope for discovery of new large orebodies would appear to be, in depth on the Red Vein, and probably in the Whin Sill; but we have to realise that extensive and expensive drilling would be required before the necessary deep sinkings could be justified. As already noted no evidence of workable ore at this horizon has yet been obtained, or seen anywhere on this vein. Although strong mineralisation has been proved by boring from Dead Friars some distance ahead of the north-east foreheads of Boltsburn Vein, if development ever takes place here it will not be through the long tunnels from Rookhope but by means of a deep sinking near the Edmundbyers road. Virgin stretches of both Boltsburn West and Wolfcleugh Old Veins still exist though both mines failed to be payable in their WSW extensions. Is the fate of the valley therefore to return to agriculture or will mining flourish again even though it has a history of 800 years of activity behind it? In any case the borehole has placed the name of Rookhope in the literature of science by persuading geologists to accept that the role of granite is to conduct heat more effectively than the rocks surrounding it and therefore to set up convective circulation of the saline ground waters which, we believe leached out and transported the Pb Zn Fba into the veins.

My grateful thanks goes to all those managers and collaborators mentioned above; full references will be found in the second edition of my British Geological Survey Memoir entitled *Geology of the Northern Pennine Orefield, Vol. 1 (Tyne to Stainmore)* 1990. For the present paper I am deeply grateful to Tony Johnson, Gerald Dresser and Carole Beaumont without whose help it could not have been prepared.

Westgarth Forster's Rule

G A L Johnson

Abstract

The rule of thickness continuity in strata first put forward by Westgarth Forster in 1809 is shown to be true for the Carboniferous Brigantian and Coal Measures strata that he investigated. These successions are formed of sedimentary cycles laid down under shallow marine and low coastal plain fluviatile conditions. Slow subsidence and steady clastic input repeatedly built up the sedimentary pile to sea level. This provided a base level control with the thickness of sediment laid down equal to subsidence and excess detritus carried away seawards in broad river channels. Stratigraphical sequences are of similar thickness over limited regions. What is lost by one bed or sequence is gained by others or *vice versa* in upward succession. The aggregate thickness of major limestone bands in the Brigantian tends to be uniform over much of northern England. The causes of deposition under Forster's Rule are described.

Westgarth Forster (1772–1835) a celebrated mining engineer and geologist, was the eldest son of Westgarth and Lucy Forster of Ivy House, Garrigill and Jeffrey's Rake, Hunstanworth. His father was a successful manager of the Blacketts' Allendale Mines and young Westgarth acted as an assistant to him and learnt the essentials of mining and surveying. On his father's death in 1797 Westgarth was asked to take on the manager's duties for the Allendale company and he held this position for over ten years. At about this time he was assembling data on the detailed stratigraphical succession in the Carboniferous rocks of the Northern Pennines and Durham Coalfield for a book which he had printed and published in Newcastle (Forster, 1809). The book came out in the same year as the first geological map of England by William Smith and was well received by miners and geologists. Forster's strata and William Smith's maps laid the foundation for a major advance in geological understanding. Westgarth was well pleased with the success of his book. It brought his name into prominence with the mining community and he became a recognised authority on geological and mining matters. He continued to collect information on mining in the north of England for a second enlarged account of Carboniferous strata with extensive sections on the discovery, opening and working of lead mines and the smelting of lead ore. The second edition was an immediate success so that in future years he planned a revised third edition, but this was not completed.

These notes on the career of Westgarth Forster are mainly taken from his biography written by the Revd W. Nall in the introduction to the third edition of Forster's *Strata* (1883). This is a faithful reproduction of the second edition of the *Strata* with only minor alterations to the text to bring it up to date. There is much of interest in this biographic account of Westgarth Forster's life and family and it can be recommended.

See also Page 19 by P. Wilkinson, (Editor)

Geological Succession

Westgarth Forster was involved with the mining industry in the north of England and had interests in the Great Northern Coalfield as well as his main work in the lead mines of Alston Moor, the Northern Pennine Orefield. In his published section of strata and the commentary that goes with it, he gives a detailed account of the stratigraphical sequence of the lead mines and the coal mines, but admits uncertainty about the intervening strata. Forster's Lead Measures and Coal Measures both belong to the Carboniferous System. The succession in the lead mines is Dinantian and Namurian while the overlying Coal Measures are Westphalian. Both sequences are formed of cycles of sedimentation or cyclothems. In the lead mines the sequence lies mainly near the top of the Dinantian in the Brigantian Stage. They are marine and fluviatile cycles with a general sequence — limestone, mudstone, sandstone, seatearth and occasionally coal, repeated ten times. The Coal Measures cycles are similar, but lack the marine limestone and mudstone; they consist of lacustrine mudstone and fluviatile sandstones with thick seatearth bands and coal seams. Each of the major limestone and sandstone bands in the Lead Measures and the workable coal seams in the Coal Measures were named by miners and quarrymen and are listed in Forster's *Strata* (1809) for the first time.

Continuity of Strata

The following general rule for the pattern of thickness changes in strata in the Lead Measures, Brigantian of the Northern Pennine Orefield, is given on page 28 of the first edition of Forster's *Strata* (1809).

'It is necessary to observe, as a general rule, that if we lose in the thickness of one stratum, we gain it in another stratum; that is to say, what we lose in plate-beds, or indurated argillaceous earths, we will gain in the limestone or hazles or siliceous and calcareous earths; so that we shall have the same thickness throughout the whole section, either in siliceous or calcareous, or argillaceous earths, and in different mining fields, or on different sides of the line of acclivity of the strata.'

In the second edition of Forster's *Strata* (1821) the rule is mentioned twice. First on page 33, in considering the Coal Measures, Forster states that the difference in thickness of strata 'are not of much consequence in a geological point of view, as they do not generally affect the aggregate depth of strata, the deficiency in the thickness of one stratum, being supplied by the redundancy of another'. Later on pages 92 and 93 he states the rule more clearly:

'In working the Lead Mines, each individual bed, is anticipated and calculated upon with great confidence, by practical miners, by whom it is received as a general rule, that what is lost in the thickness of one Stratum, is, very often, gained in another; that is to say, what is lost in Plate beds or indurated Argillaceous earths, is generally gained in the Limestones or Hazles, or the Calcareous and Siliceous parts of the Strata; so that the same thickness is produced throughout the section, by the Siliceous, Calcareous, and Argillaceous earths, taken together.'

In the third edition of Forster's *Strata* edited by Nall (1883), the references to continuity in the thickness of strata in the Coal Measures and in the lead mines are copied verbatim from the second edition.

Confirmation of Forster's Rule

Forster's rule of continuity of the thickness of strata in the Pennines and North East Coalfield was not taken up by later workers. It was accepted by miners in Northern England and no longer of interest to academic geologists. However, lateral continuity of thickness of the Productive Coal Measures in the North East Coalfield was used to predict workable coal seams

a stratigraphical study by Rowley (1969, p. 347). He shows that the total thickness of Brigantian strata, referred to by him as the Middle Limestone Group, the thickness of clastic deposits (mudstone and sandstone) and the thickness of limestone is remarkably uniform from east to west across the northern Pennines. Further, whereas the clastic rocks thin westwards off the Alston Block and thicken both northwards and southwards, the total limestone thickness is almost constant throughout the region. Over the relatively stable Alston Block, continuity of stratal thickness obeys Forster's Rule according to Rowley's figures, but he did not refer to Forster's work in his paper.

		Brigantian Stage	Total Brigantian Clastic Rocks	Total Brigantian Limestone
Cross Fell	(Johnson & Dunham 1963)	242	177	65
Meldon Hill & High Cup	(Burgess & Holliday 1979)	243	183	60
Croglin Water	(Trotter & Hollingworth 1932)	274	210	64
Tyne Head & Moor House	(Johnson & Dunham 1963)	220	162	58
Grass Hill & Cow Green	(Dunham 1990)	230	173	57
Allenheads No. 1 Borehole	(Dunham 1990)	260	202	58
Rookhope Borehole	(Dunham et al 1965)	263	201	62
Roddymoor Borehole	(Woolacott 1923)	268	188	80

Table I   Thickness of the Brigantian Stage on the Alston Block (metres)

extending under the North Sea (Hickling, 1949, p. 661). He states that over a north to south distance of 80 km across the coalfield, the thickness of strata between the High Main and the Brockwell coals is rarely less than 213 m or more than 260 m. The general uniformity is very pronounced with little systematic variation in the thickness of the Coal Measures. Deposition of strata between adjacent marker bands varies greatly, but over the entire period of deposition, irregular subsidences were evened-out, producing a relatively constant total thickness of strata. This is striking support for Forster's observations on the Coal Measures in Northumberland and Durham, but Hickling does not mention Westgarth Forster because he gives no references to previous work.

An analysis of Brigantian Cyclothems, Forster's Lead Measures, in the Northern Pennines was produced by Professor Sir Kingsley Dunham (1950) in a paper on Lower Carboniferous sedimentation which cites Forster's work. His figures support Forster's view that variation in the thickness of mudstone is compensated by variation in the thickness of sandstone which he brings out by showing that the variation in thickness of sandstones is, in many cyclothems, greater than the variation in the cyclothem as a whole. He also shows that limestone bands have a small variation in thickness as compared to the interbedded clastic sediments, mudstone and sandstone.

A further account of variation in thickness of Brigantian Cyclothems in the Northern Pennines, was produced as part of

Eight long sections from natural exposures, boreholes and mine workings on the Alston Block are given in Table I. The thickness of the Brigantian on the block varies between 220 m and 274 m with evidence of systematic increase towards the margins in all directions except to the west into the Vale of Eden. Possibly the succession thins over the centre of the block at Tynehead and Cow Green. Variation in the Brigantian sequence is caused by changes in the clastic content because the total thickness of limestone remains relatively constant. If we omit the Roddymoor Borehole, which was drilled 75 years ago and the thickness of limestone rather than calcareous shale may be exaggerated, the total thickness of the block varies between 57 m and 65 m, a range of only 8 m. These figures support the findings of Dunham (1950) and Rowley (1969) on the constant thickness of limestone and supports Forster's contention that the thickness of the Brigantian is fairly constant over the Alston Block.

Forster's Rule can be investigated further by comparison of the thicknesses of beds in a long Brigantian sequence. The Rookhope Borehole was chosen for this study as it sections the full succession and is cut by only one significant fault, the Red Vein, the throw of which is known. The borehole was drilled at Rookhope in Weardale in 1960–61 to prove the Carboniferous succession and the underlying Weardale Granite (Dunham *et al.* 1965). As elsewhere, the Brigantian sequence in the borehole is composed of 10 cycles of sedimentation or cyclothems each consisting of the general sequence: limestone, mudstone, sandstone, seatearth and rarely coal. This is the sequence that Forster called the Lead Measures and found to be of constant thickness and where thick and thin beds of strata compensate each other.

The sequence of ten cyclothems in the Rookhope Borehole with thicknesses is given in Table II. In this table the limestone is the major band at the base of cyclothems and does not include the thin limestone bands that may be developed towards the top of the cycles. The mudstone division lies above the limestone and grades upwards to siltstone and interbedded mudstone, siltstone and fine- grained sandstone; it ends against the sandstone division. The sandstone may continue to the top of the cyclothem, but more often it grades to interbedded mudstone, sandstone and seatearth which are included in the sandstone division in Table II.

cycles only slightly above the mean. No simple relationship exists between small and large cycles, but rather compensation takes place throughout the whole succession.

Major limestone bands in the Rookhope Borehole vary between 1.86 m and 9.32 m thick with a mean of 5.73 m (Table II, column c). Irregular alternation of limestone bands of above and below the mean thickness is conspicuous (Table II, column g). Four thicker limestones are compensated by six limestones of below average thickness. It is noteworthy that the thicker limestones tend to lie in the lower half of the succession.

Mudstone bands in the borehole vary from less than 1 m to 13.96 m with a mean thickness of 6.4 m (Table II, column b). Of about the same degree of variation, the sandstone division is between 7.01 m and 20.17 m thick with a mean of 13.49 m.

Cyclothems	Thickness (metres)				Variation about the mean (metres)			
	a Sandstone	b Mudstone	c Limestone	d Cyclothem	e Sandstone	f Mudstone	g Limestone	h Cyclothem
Four Fathom	20.13	12.79	5.71	38.63	+6.00	+6.39	−0.02	+12.37
Three Yard	13.56	13.96	2.5	30.02	−0.57	+7.56	−3.23	+3.76
Five Yard	7.01	6.92	4.9	18.83	−7.12	+0.52	−0.83	−7.43
Scar	15.44	8.37	9.13	32.94	+1.31	+1.97	+3.4	+6.68
Single Post†	20.33	1.01	1.86	23.2	+6.20	−5.39	−3.87	−3.06
Tyne Bottom*	16.3	5.38	9.32	31.0	+2.17	−1.02	+3.59	+4.74
Jew	20.17	1.79	7.57	29.53	+6.04	−4.61	+1.84	+3.27
Lower Little	7.99	1.49	4.65	14.13	−6.14	−4.91	−1.08	−12.13
Smiddy	12.11	11.58	8.08	31.77	−2.02	+5.18	+2.35	+5.51
Peghorn	8.28	0.71	3.61	12.60	−5.85	−5.69	−2.12	−13.66
Total	141.3	64.0	57.3	262.6				
Average	14.13	6.40	5.73	26.26				

Table II
Thickness of Brigantian Cyclothems & their sandstone, mudstone & limestone units in the Rookhope Borehole, with variation about mean values
*The Tyne Bottom Cyclothem is cut by the Red Vein in the borehole causing a loss of 16.5 m of clastic rocks.
The cycle is reconstructed to the full thickness in this table.
†The Cockle Shell Limestone is now regarded as a minor limestone band within the Single Post Cyclothem (Johnson & Nudds, 1996)

The Brigantian cyclothems of the Rookhope Borehole vary in thickness between 12.6 m and 38.63 m with a mean thickness of 26.26 m (Table II). Only the Peghorn cycle at the base is less than half the mean thickness and it may be transitional with the underlying simple Asbian cycles. In the borehole the cycles vary in thickness about the mean by irregular alternation. Thus if cycles below the mean are called small (s) and those above the mean large (l), the sequence from the base upwards (Table II, column d) is:

$$s - l - s - l - l - s - l - s - l - l$$

Broadly in Forster's terms what is lost by one cyclothem is gained by others. This variation is given quantitatively in Table II, column h, where positive or negative variation of the cyclothems about the mean is given in metres. Two cycles well below average thickness in the lower part of the succession (Peghorn and Lower Little) with two other small cycles are compensated by the large Four Fathom cycle and five other

The mudstone does not alternate in thickness, but there is a systematic trend of below average thickness in the lower part of the succession and above average thickness towards the top of the sequence (Table II, columns b and f). The sandstone division shows the same pattern of behaviour, but the thickness of sandstone is related to the thickness of the underlying mudstone or the thickness of the cyclothem. The aggregate thickness of mudstone and sandstone in cyclothems shows the same pattern of variation as the cyclothems themselves; thickness of clastic sediment is directly related to the thickness of the cyclothem. In addition to these trends, four cycles with either above or below average mudstone and sandstone compare with six cycles with either high sandstone and low mudstone or low sandstone and high mudstone (Table II, columns e and f). There is a trend in the cyclothems for what is lost in mudstone to be made up in sandstone or *vice versa* as Forster recognised, but in cycles of above average or below average thickness this trend is masked.

15

Using the notation already employed, below average thickness (s) and above average thickness (l), the variation in sandstone, mudstone and limestone divisions of the Rookhope Borehole is given below (Table II, columns a, b and c).

Sandstone $- s - s - s - l - l - l - l - s - s - l$
Mudstone $- s - l - s - s - s - s - l - l - l - l$
Limestone $- s - l - s - l - l - s - l - s - s - s$

In the diagram, the left hand column is the Peghorn Cyclothem and the right hand column is the Four Fathom. Only the Peghorn and the Lower Little are below average in all of the divisions and only the Scar is above average in all divisions. The other seven cycles contain divisions that are both above and below average thickness that compensate within each of the cyclothems according to Forster's Rule. In addition there is a general systematic trend for limestones to thin and mudstones and sandstones to thicken in upward succession.

Controls of Forster's Rule Deposition

Deposition under Forster's Rule, that what is lost by one bed is gained by another so that a constant thickness of the succession is maintained, is an unusual pattern of sedimentation associated with the Brigantian of the Alston Block and the Coal Measures of North East England. Special controls of deposition are required to establish and maintain this regime of sedimentation. No one mechanism is likely to be responsible for all the features of Forster's Rule deposition and rather a number of independent causes acting together would be expected. Controls for constant Brigantian thickness, constant aggregate limestone thickness and alternation of thickness of beds of strata will be discussed in the following paragraphs.

1. The relatively constant thickness of the Brigantian Stage over the Alston Block and the remarkable lack of variation in thickness of the Productive Coal Measures in the North East Coalfield, both recognised by Forster and later workers, must have an underlying cause. In both cases deltaic sediments were being laid down either over a shallow marine lower deltaic plain or a flat fluviatile upper deltaic plain. The Brigantian alternated between lower and upper delta plain deposition while the Coal Measures were formed over a wide upper delta plain with few short marine episodes. In both cases, separated by a long interval of time, the flat delta plain, almost at sea level, stretched widely over the whole of northern England. Regional subsidence affected all of northern England at this time and caused shallow marine transgressions and the formation of shallow lake basins. Deposition took place fortuitously when subsidence caused depressions to form over the delta plain. Clastic sediment, entering the region from the uplands to the north and east, was of greater volume than the amount of subsidence so that excess sediment was carried seawards across the area in broad river channels some of which are known (Hodge and Dunham, 1991). Owing to this form of base level control (Barrell, 1917), excess sediment was carried across the delta plain and neither deposition nor erosion took place. Thus thickness of deposition equalled depth of subsidence. If the amount of subsidence is uniform over a region, an equal thickness of sediments would be laid down over the area. Under these limiting conditions, the Brigantian of the Alston Block and the Coal Measures of North East England were laid down.

2. The Brigantian cyclothems and the Coal Measures cyclothems have uniform aggregate thickness that equals the depth of subsidence as in paragraph 1 above, but in addition to this the number of cyclothems is constant throughout the region. There are ten Brigantian cyclothems over the Alston Block and 14 Coal Measures cyclothems in the North East Coalfield. The cyclothems vary considerably in thickness, perhaps because in some areas they are starved of clastic sediment, but what is lost by one cycle is gained by others and *vice versa* in upward succession so that the aggregate thickness of the full succession remains the same.

3. Alteration in thickness of strata under Forster's Rule, what is lost by mudstone is gained by sandstone etc., takes place under the constraints listed under paragraphs 1 and 2. But when individual lithological divisions are considered the constant sequence of strata within the cyclothems becomes important. The Brigantian cyclothems have the broad sequence limestone, mudstone, sandstone and seatearth, while the Coal Measures cyclothems are formed of a less regular sequence of mudstone, sandstone, seatearth and coal. As the order of lithologies is maintained in each of the cycles to a large extent, a thin mudstone allows a thick sandstone to form or a thick mudstone limits the thickness of the overlying sandstone division. Local starving of clastic sediment and small variations in the pattern of subsidence may produce the irregular succession of thick and thin beds that is found in long sections (Table II). None the less, what is lost in one bed is made up by another as Forster rightly appreciated.

4. Individual major limestone bands vary in thickness, but the aggregate thickness of major limestones in the Brigantian maintains constant thickness over the Alston Block and more widely over northern England. Some additional constraint on sedimentation, over and above those listed in paragraphs 1 to 3 above, is needed to produce constant aggregate limestone thickness. Limestones differ from clastic rocks in that they accumulate at the site of deposition with little transport of carbonate materials. Rate of deposition and thickness of carbonate beds depends on the abundance and rate of growth of lime-fixing animals and plants. Northern England was situated centrally in the tropics in Carboniferous times and marine carbonate platforms formed readily in warm, shallow shelf seas. Animal and plant life were luxuriant as testified by the many macro- and microfossils found in the limestones. Under these favourable conditions, accumulation of carbonate was relatively fast and the rate of deposition must have been almost uniform over northern England. Like other beds, what is lost in one limestone is gained by others so that the same time interval for limestone deposition is maintained during the Brigantian in northern England. With uniform rate of carbonate accumulation and constant time interval for its deposition, the aggregate thickness of major limestone bands laid down during the Brigantian will also be uniform over the region.

Undoubtedly Forster (1809, 1821) was right in his findings about aggregate thickness of strata and alternation of thin and thick beds in the Brigantian of the Alston Block and the Coal Measures of the North East Coalfield. What he did not know was that this type of uniform deposition was unusual and mainly confined to northern England. Hickling (1949) recognised that deposition was of uniform thickness in the Coal Measures of Durham and Northumberland and made comparisons with other British coalfields where striking variability is found. Accepted by miners, quarrymen and geologists in the north of England, Forster's and Hickling's findings did not attract the attention of workers elsewhere in Britain, probably because they could find no evidence of uniformity of deposition in their successions. A feature of Carboniferous deposition that did generate wide interest was the occurrence and formation of Brigantian cyclothems, but this is another story (see Dunham (1950) and Leeder and Strudwick (1987)).

References

BARRELL J. 'Rhythms and the measurement of geologic time'. *Geol. Soc. America Bull.* (1917), 28, 745–904.

BURGESS I C, and HOLLIDAY D W. *Geology of the country around Brough-under-Stainmore.* (Mem. Geol. Surv. GB, 1979).

DUNHAM K C. 'Lower Carboniferous sedimentation in the Northern Pennines (England)'. *Rep. 18th Int. Geol. Congr. London (1950),* part 4, 46–63.

DUNHAM K C. *Geology of the Northern Pennine Orefield, Volume 1 Tyne to Stainmore,* 2nd ed., (Econ. Mem. Brit. Geol. Surv. 1990).

DUNHAM K C, DUNHAM A C, HODGE B L, & JOHNSON G A L. 'Granite beneath Viséan sediments with mineralization at Rookhope, Northern Pennines'. *Q. J. Geol. Soc. London (1965),* 121, 383–417.

FORSTER W. *A treatise on a section of strata commencing near Newcastle-upon-Tyne and concluding on the west side of the Mountain of Cross Fell, with remarks on mineral veins in general.* 1st ed., (Newcastle, Preston and Heaton, 1809).

FORSTER W. *A Treatise on a section of strata from Newcastle-upon-Tyne to the Mountain of Cross Fell in Cumberland; with remarks on mineral veins in general,* 2nd ed. (Alston, Westgarth Forster, 1821).

FORSTER W. (3rd edition), edited with revisions by NALL W. (Newcastle, Andrew Reid, 1883).

HICKLING H G A. 'Prospects of undersea coalfield extension in the North-East'. *Trans. Inst. Mining Engineers (1949),* 109, 659–674.

HODGE B L, & DUNHAM K C. 'Clastics, coals, palaeodistributaries and mineralisation in the Namurian Great Cyclothem, Northern Pennines and Northumberland Trough'. *Proc. Yorkshire Geol. Soc.* (1991), 48, 323–337.

JOHNSON G A L, & DUNHAM K C. *The Geology of Moor House.* Nature Conservancy Monograph No. 2, (London HMSO, 1963).

JOHNSON G A L, & NUDDS J R. 'Carboniferous biostratigraphy of the Rookhope Borehole, Co. Durham'. *Trans. Roy. Soc. Edinburgh (1996),* 86, 181–226.

LEEDER M R, & STRUDWICK A E. 'Delta-marine interactions: a discussion of sedimentary models for Yoredale-type cyclicity in the Dinantian of Northern England'. In MILLER J, ADAMS A E, & WRIGHT V P. *European Dinantian Environments.* (Chichester, John Wiley, 1987), 115–130.

ROWLEY C R. 'The stratigraphy of the Carboniferous Middle Limestone Group of west Edenside, Westmorland'. *Proc. Yorkshire Geol. Soc. (1969)* 37, 329–350.

TROTTER F M, & HOLLINGWORTH S E. *The Geology of the Brampton district.* (Mem. Geol. Surv. GB, 1932).

WOOLACOTT D. 'On a boring at Roddymoor Colliery near Crook, Co. Durham'. *Geol. Mag.* (1923) 609, 50–62.

Leadmining Families — The Westgarths and the Forsters

Peter Wilkinson

Synopsis.

Little accurate information has appeared regarding the early life and work of Westgarth Forster Junior, surveyor, mining engineer, geologist and author of the famous *Treatise on a Section of the Strata* and even less concerning his family background and connections.

This article traces various family members, examining their involvement in the lead mining industry of the North Pennines during the eighteenth century, as well as demonstrating their cumulative influence on the work of the famous author.

It is a mixture of family history and a miscellany of lead mining facts extracted, where possible, from primary source material.

The Blacketts, the W.B. Lead Company and the London Lead Company.

A brief history of those members of the Blackett family connected with lead mining, their Company and the London Lead Company is first given to allow a fuller comprehension of the industrial structure within which the Westgarths and the Forsters were employed.

From the first Sir William Blackett who died in 1680 came the Matfen and Wallington sides of the family, it being the latter who are of general concern here. His son Sir William Blackett II purchased the Hexhamshire Estates which included the Allendales from the Fenwick family in 1689, giving him control of a large tract of lead mining ground. He also became involved in Weardale in 1696 when he took the Moormaster lease from the Bishop of Durham, effectively giving him command of much of the lead mining in that valley. Upon his death in 1705, the estates passed to his son Sir William III who died without legitimate issue in 1728. He devised his property to his illegitimate daughter Elizabeth Ord on the condition that she married his nephew Walter Calverley within a year and took the name of Blackett. Sir Walter Calverley Blackett succeeded to his father's Baronetcy in 1749 and died in 1777. On his death the estates were again split, Wallington going to his sister Julia's family, the Trevelyans and the remainder, including the lead mining interests, to Sir Thomas Wentworth Blackett of Bretton Park near Wakefield. He died in 1792, leaving the property and lead mining concerns to his illegitimate daughter Diana, who had married Colonel Thomas Richard Beaumont. The estates remained under their joint control until his death in 1829.

Unlike the Blackett family history, the structure and administration of the lead mining company is quite straightforward. Although some of the owners took a close interest in the business, effective control lay in the hands of the Chief Agent who had offices at Pilgrim Street in Newcastle-upon-Tyne. The first noted was Joseph Richmond, who was appointed in the mid 1720s and remained in place until he died in April 1763. He was assisted for many years by his son Henry who took over the position at a salary of £200 p.a. when his father died and remained in charge until his death in May 1776. Both the Richmonds give the impression of being quiet,

efficient and reasonable men with a degree of caution, patience and tact. The opposite appears true of the Chief Agent who followed in 1777 — the irascible and sometimes unscrupulous John Erasmus Blackett, himself a member of the Matfen side of the family, who retained the post on a salary of £210 p.a. until removed in December 1804. Under his agency the profits increased enormously but often at some risk to the owners. He suffered from rheumatism and neuralgia and died in 1814 aged 86 years. These Chief Agents though not expert in any particular field, controlled and advised on almost every aspect of their employer's business, as well as superintending the mills, mines and finances of the mining concerns. During the eighteenth and early nineteenth centuries the mines were divided into three geographical districts, each controlled by a Principal Agent or Chief Grove Steward. The Weardale district had its headquarters at Newhouse near Ireshopeburn, West Allendale was controlled from Coalcleugh and East Allendale from Allenheads. These areas were not always strictly adhered to since Killhope at the head of the Wear valley was, prior to 1762, run by the Allenheads agent, but after that time came under the control of the Coalcleugh district. Similarly it was more convenient to manage Wolfcleugh in the Rookhope valley from Allenheads rather than Ireshopeburn. The Principal Agents in each district were normally supported by a Second and Third Agent, with the Killhope sub-district sometimes having a separate assistant. These Agents were responsible for the daily management and general development of the mines within their area, including the ore carriage to the mills and the keeping of full accounts and records.

On the smelting side of the business, authority devolved from the Senior Mill Agent based at Dukesfield, the largest of the mills, situated near Slaley in Hexhamshire. The mills at Rookhope, Allenheads and later, Allendale, were each under the management of a Mill Clerk, sometimes supported by an assistant, who were also responsible for lead carriage and keeping accounts. Although some of the mills had attached refineries, there was in addition on Tyneside a large refinery at Blaydon under the control of a Refining Agent or Clerk. In the nineteenth century the Senior Mill Agent operated from that place and not from Dukesfield as before.

Early records indicate that the Quaker controlled Ryton Company had leased mines on the Priorsdale Estate around Tynehead in about 1695, together with a cupola and refinery at Blaydon-on-Tyne. During the period 1695–1704, the company was closely associated with the Society of Royal Mines Copper, after which an amalgamation took place through a complicated share transfer to form the London Lead Company. This new company then had an important smelting charter in its hands under which it was to operate successfully until its final closure in 1905. In the Northern Pennines the London Lead Company (also known as the Governor & Co. and the Quaker Co.) first took leases in the Tynehead area, near Garrigill on Alston Moor. A Directors' report of 1706 named these mines as New Tyne Green, Old Tyne Green, Covert Fold, Clargill Head,

Longhole Head, with part shares in Fairhill and Blagill. From this nucleus of workings near Garrigill, the company spread out across the North Pennines taking a number of mine leases in the Blanchland area during the period 1708–31 and building smelt mills at Acton and Jeffreys within that district. This compact group of Derwent leases became an important and flourishing part of the Company and were retained until 1806. Many Quakers were connected with the newly formed London Lead Company, but others had been involved with that company's predecessors, the Ryton Smelting Co., for it is more than coincidence that Quaker families then existed in that inhospitable part of the country, setting up meeting houses at Alston and Nenthead in the early eighteenth century. It is within this framework that the careers of the Westgarths and the Fosters are considered.

The Westgarth Family
Any examination of the original association between the Westgarth and the Forster families should have been straightforward, as previous writers have noted close ties with the Westgarths of Unthank and Stanhope in Weardale. This important and prolific family took the Unthank Estate from the Maddisons prior to 1640 and continued there until the death of John Westgarth in 1781, after which time it passed to his three daughters and eventually out of Westgarth ownership. John Westgarth was involved in lead mining and therefore had close links with the Blackett family, Moormasters, and mine operators in Weardale from whom he obtained a number of leases. His opinion on local matters appears to have been much valued, as he was regularly consulted by the Blackett Company's Chief Agent. Westgarth Forster Snr. reputedly married a member of the Weardale Emerson family and he died at Unthank Hall in 1797, although he was the lessee of the property and never the owner. These and other apparently related facts have suggested the close connections with the Unthank Westgarths. Available records, however, indicate no obvious associations with either of the above noted Weardale families.

If not from Weardale then where did the Westgarths originate? Early parish registers show small groups at Ousby, Brampton and Alston Moor. At the latter place they appear in Garrigill and Blagill, both locations being closely associated with lead mining. No satisfactory pedigree could initially be proved here as family members appeared and disappeared without continuity, several being married out of the area. The later obituary notice of William Westgarth described him as '… one of those people called Quakers …',[1] indicating the reason for the irregular register entries. From 1538 parish priests were required to keep records of baptisms, marriages and deaths within their area, later including those for nonconformists and for any ceremonies which took place outside the parish. Mistakes and omissions often occur with few entries relating to Quakers, who usually insisted on conducting their own rituals and keeping their own records. A short list of Quaker families closely coincides with several abnormal entries seen in parish registers, so allowing an outline Westgarth pedigree to be constructed.[2] With this and other supportive information a family emanating from the upper South Tyne valley with associated members in the nearby Nent valley can be traced.

It appears likely that the Westgarths were involved with early lead mining developments taking place under the emerging London Lead Company in the Tynehead area, near Garrigill on Alston Moor. William Westgarth of Low Cragg, South Tynedale, married Jane Little of Garrigill in 1702,[3] she was probably the person noted in the Hunstanworth (Blanchland) parish register in May 1751 under the entry: '… Jane Westgarth, an old woman from Jeffrys Rake, Buried …'. This was typical of an 'abnormal' entry as no details of her family were given, suggesting in this case that she was a Quaker. No record of William's death has been seen. Of their six children, three are of relevance: Thomas, Mary and Hannah. Hannah's marriage recorded at Hunstanworth, the entry for 31 July 1735 being '… Emmanuel Paulfroman & Hannah Westgarth of Jeffrys was married … at the Church …' is again an 'odd' entry. The Paulfromans were a mining family working for the London Lead Company at Blanchland and were almost certainly Quakers. Her sister Mary Westgarth of Jeffreys Rake, of whom no register details have been seen, married George Forster (Foster or Forrester) of Hexhamshire, at Hexham on 26th October 1736, also going through a second ceremony two days later which was recorded in the Hunstanworth register under the heading of '… Marriages Clandistinly at Lamely by Edmund Baxter 1736 …'. His name was written as Forrester and another Paulfroman, Robert, is also shown in the short list of external marriages. The above marriage of Mary Westgarth, the daughter of William of Garrigill and George Forster represented the original union of these two families, their firstborn son being named Westgarth.

Thomas, the eldest son of William, married Elizabeth Kinnlasyde (Keenleyside) in April 1731, and are shown by a rental list to be living at Jeffrey's Rake Hunstanworth in late 1734.[4] They must however, have resided at that place earlier as sons William (who died at birth) and John were born there in 1732 and 1733. Many Kinnlasydes were resident in Allendale, but a number lived and worked at Blanchland and as they too appear in clandestine marriages, were possibly Quakers. It is likely that William Westgarth Snr. had died before the move to Hunstanworth as Thomas appears as the tenant and was accompanied by at least two of his sisters and possibly his mother Jane. The next available list is for 1749–50 and shows no Westgarths as tenants.

Thomas, brother of Mary and Hannah was a senior mining Agent and engineer with the London Lead Company, his name appearing regularly in their records for the period 1737–48.[5] That he was in charge of the Blanchland district for the company is indicated by individual entries for his salary: Jeffrys Mill £5 p.a., Acton Mill £10 p.a., Jeffrys Mine £20 p.a. and Shildon Mine £15 p.a. giving a total of £50 p.a., a substantial sum at that time. He was also paid for 'engine keeping' as well as supplying candles and timber. More interesting perhaps are payments for his journeys around the British Isles, checking on the company's mines and smelt mills and examining sites for new developments. These include in 1736–7, Gadlis and various silver mines in Wales, Winster and Wensley in Derbyshire, and at least two trips to Ireland.[6] The following year is a payment of £46 for visits to Limerick and London. Up to 1732 the four main shareholders had controlled the London Lead Company business doing much of the work themselves, but after that date a new group of directors were installed who brought fresh vigour and impetus to the concern and Thomas can be seen as a part of that more rapid and widespread expansion. Detailed accounts continue up to his last salary payment entered on 24th December 1740, after which time his name appears against other items such as ore purchases, lead sales and the supply of materials. The last account entry shown on 27th August 1748 corresponds closely with the date recorded for his death of July 1748. He was then resident in East Allendale at 'Rideing' where three of his children were born. He was buried nearby at the Wooley Burnfoot Meeting House.[7] Although no salary details were recorded for the last few years of his life, he obviously continued as a senior Agent as can be seen from a volume of his plans and reports dated 1740-2[8] which show mines at Blagill and Clargill on Alston Moor, Wanlockhead in Scotland and Wensley and Winster, the latter being executed in connection with his purchase of working ground there for the company in 1743.

Of Thomas Westgarth's five sons, William became a celebrated engineer, most famous for his invention of the hydraulic engine. He was born in March 1735 at Jeffreys Rake at Hunstanworth and was brought up as a Quaker and although only 13 years old when his father died, he undoubtedly learned much from him. As was then commonplace, Agents' sons by working as assistants to their fathers from an early age acquired a valuable store of practical knowledge which often later allowed them to inherit their parents position. William became an Agent with the London Lead Company and moved to Alston Moor where he married Jane Wilkinson in September 1759. She was probably the daughter of Jacob Wilkinson of the Hill, a farm near Garrigill, with close relations living at the adjoining properties of the Hole and Ashgillside. Her baptism was shown as a normal entry in the St John's Church register at Garrigill along with other members of her family, indicating that they were Anglicans. Their marriage entry in the Alston St Augustine's register is however abnormal in that it is out of date order and reads: '... William Westgarth and Jane Wilkinson, both of the parish of Alston were married at Dumfries in Scotland, the 17th September 1759 as appear by a certificate attested by John Brown, William Faber and Thomas Seet ...' (or Scot). The entry following, though ten years later in May 1769, shows a similar circumstance with Joshua Westgarth, William's younger brother, marrying Jane Hilton at Gretna Green. Jane Hilton was not a Quaker and it would appear that both the above marriages were conducted by a priest. Records show that in the Alston area at that time, many young Quaker couples preferred a church ceremony to that of their own establishment much against the wishes of their elders. It is likely that William chose Dumfries to get married as he was familiar with that area having worked at or visited the London Lead Company mines at Wanlockhead.

The three known children of William and Jane were born at Nenthead, Thomas in 1760, William in 1762, and Mary in 1764. Only William Jnr. was later noted working in the mining industry, employed by the W. B. Lead Co. He became Assistant Smelting Agent to the famous Isaac Hunter Jnr. at Dukesfield Mill in April 1786, taking over from Mr Salkeld who suffered '... a Stroke of the Palsy ...'.[9] By the time of the 1805 W. B.

Lead Co. reorganisation, Hunter had left his Dukesfield agency, his place later being taken by William Jnr. at a salary of £100 p.a. although still second in seniority to Robert Mulcaster, the newly appointed Chief Smelting Agent based at Blaydon Refinery. William remained in that post until his death in December 1809 aged 47 years. He is buried in Slaley churchyard along with his mother Jane who died in 1814 aged 81 years. Though William Snr., the ingenious engineer, followed his father Thomas as an Agent for the London Lead Company, his later years were spent in the employment of the W. B. Lead Co. as Principal Agent or Chief Grove Steward at Coalcleugh in West Allendale.

William Westgarth at Coalcleugh.

In tracing William Westgarth's later career some examination has been made of the W. B. Lead Co. records, in particular the Quarterly Accounts for Coalcleugh and the Chief Agents Letter Books.[10] As no precise date was available for him entering Blackett employment, the search began with the year 1753, these being the earliest extant accounts for Coalcleugh. It is apparent that the Coalcleugh district was not only the most important of the Blackett mining areas at that time, but the technical developments taking place there were well in advance of other regions. There is much confusion in published works regarding the individual achievements of the two cousins, William Westgarth and Westgarth Forster; both are credited with the introduction of long levels and wagonways, the use of rails and horses underground and the invention of the hydraulic engine. As Coalcleugh was at the forefront of local technological development at that time, these innovations are detailed here chronologically.

There are many claims for pre-eminence in the introduction of underground railways and wagonways within the Lead Dales but it would appear that the W. B. Lead Co. should be credited with this development. Long levels or horizontal drifts were not a new idea having been used in some areas for drainage purposes but not for access or development of the mines. In a Greenwich Hospital Moormasters report of 1821, referring to the Nent Force Level on Alston Moor is the statement: '... in which was first laid a Railway for bringing out the work in a Wagon by a Horse, which example was soon followed by other Mining Companies.'[11] As the Nent Force Level was not begun until 1776 it was certainly not the first, nor was the practice common until a much later date. Larger schemes for level and wagonway development in the London Lead Company mines were introduced in the post-1790 era at Nenthead by Thomas Dodd but during the earlier period they made use of Blackett wagonways for drawing work from the boundary area of Rampgill Mine. Prior to the introduction of underground railways the miners relied on sledges, wheel-barrows and kibbles to remove ore and deads in mines designed to operate mainly by shafts and whimseys.

An entry in the Coalcleugh account books for the quarter October to December 1753 states: '... Thomas Farbridge for 5 wagon wheels @ 27d—11/3d' followed in January–March by: '... Masons walling the Horse Level mouth, winning stones etc ...' with a list of nineteen men: '... casting and serving the masons with stones ...' all clear indications that a horse operated underground wagonway was begun not later than

1753. In April–June 1754 the accounts show payments for '... wagon horse backskins ...' and '... getting down a shaft to the Horse Level ...' together with payments to Thomas Armstrong for '... drawing deads out of East and West Levels and emptying the Waggons 68 shifts 5 waggons ...'. Such entries may suggest an even earlier starting date to the scheme than the supposed six months previous. There is near accuracy in Thomas Sopwith's statement regarding horse levels when he wrote: '... This superior mode of working mines is said to have been first introduced into the country by Sir Walter Calverley Blackett about the year 1760, but not generally adopted for many years ...'.[12]

There are no clues in the records seen as to where the new technology came from, though the northern coalfields would seem to be the most obvious answer. However the date of the first use of horses on underground roadways in coal mines is also a contentious issue, with suggestions ranging from the first half of the eighteenth century,[13] up to 1763.[14] M. Gabriel Jars visited both Tyneside coal mines and Coalcleugh lead mines in 1765 and remarked on the similarity of the systems then in use. Thomas Armstrong, the Coalcleugh Principal Agent at that time does not appear to have been particularly outstanding, as the Chief Agent's letter to Sir Walter for 9th July 1756 notes: '... Thom. Armstrong, Steward at Coalcleugh died on Sunday last with, I think, no great loss to yourself ...'. In the Account Books the system can be seen to be developing, for in January–March 1755 there are entries for: '... Wagemen (or Woodmen?) laying Wagon Rails ...' and in April–June: '... John Curry for Making and Mending Waggons ... leading deads out of East and West Levels, 241 shifts @ 2/6d .... emptying the waggons 125 shifts 1 wagon ...'. These last two payments were to the Agent, Thomas Armstrong, who supplied the men and horses for drawing the wagons. This practice lasted well into the nineteenth century in all the major companies, with Agents subsidising their salaries by supplying labour and horses for both level and whimsey shaft drawing work, becoming a generally accepted and necessary part of the system in which most Agents were involved. The specific entries over the next fifty years indicate that horses were only used on main levels designed for that purpose and almost without exception the animals were supplied by the Agents. The method of measuring by wagon shifts was a contemporary innovation and probably then consisted of 8 wagons per shift, giving a total of 1928 wagonloads of deads for the entry mentioned above. The charge of 2/6d. was for man and horse, the rates later varying between 3/6d. and 4/8d. depending on the distance hauled. Whilst promoting new practices, another entry for April–June 1755 is worth note: '... James Stott for building Asay Furnace for trying the ore and lead, 7 days at 18d ....'.

Thomas Armstrong was replaced as Principal Agent in July 1756 by a relative, Robert Harrison, another local man of private means who owned a small estate. The dead Agent's son, George Armstrong, remained as Second Agent. Shortly after Harrison's arrival there were signs of renewed vigour in the working of the Coalcleugh mines and substantial developments began taking place, the increased movement of materials and references to new trials indicating a period of expansion. Some of the most interesting yet puzzling Account Book entries for

this period concern the carriage of dozens of loads of wagon rails either direct from Dukesfield or from the depot at Limestone Brae, which are paid for by weight. For example in July–September 1756: '... Carrick for carriage of wagon rails from Dukesfield to Coalcleugh 32 pieces is 107½ stone @ 1d. per stone ... Will. Parker ditto 23 pieces is 69 stone ...'—the lists for this and the following year amounting to hundreds of pieces of rail, each with an average weight of about 3 stone. Later, in 1757 ten men spent 318 work-days loading rails at Limestone Brea depot, together with several loads of wagon wheels. Carriage by the stone clearly indicates iron rail being transported from the east side of the country, although the first record of the production of cast-iron rail is from Coalbrookdale in Shropshire, ten years later in 1767. One possible explanation is that the rail referred to here was 'second rail' or iron strip attached to the top of previously laid wooden rail, an idea which originated in the north-east coalfield in about 1740, but was nevertheless very advanced for the North Pennine orefield. The increased mine activity is explained in a letter of December 1756 from the Chief Agent to Robert Harrison, which ends: '... I wish you every success with your new level ...' and an entry in the Account Books: '... Labourers drawing deads out of the way to the new level at Low Coalcleugh ...'. Subsequent entries note payments to large partnerships of men working in '... Low Coalcleugh New Level ...'. That a carefully planned scheme was in motion is suggested by the entry recording the re-opening of Shield Ridge Old Level, originally begun in 1684 as a drainage level, itself at that time a pioneering project. Harrison's idea to clean out and extend this drift along the length of Low Coalcleugh Vein and so keep the strata drained below his new horse level was obviously successful as regular entries for sludging and cleaning over the next 50 years indicate. Many entries appear during 1757 and 1758 for both fathoms of wagon rails and sawing wagon rails, suggesting that some wooden rails were being used in the main New Level and the side drifts: '... Woodmen and others laying wagon rails and trailing them up the level ... John Todd for 250 fathoms of wagon rails, ditto for 30 dozen sleepers @ 28d. per doz ... William Surtees and Co sawing wagon rails at Dukesfield, 24 days @ 16d. per day ... John Walton for 577 fathoms of rail @ 10d. per fathom, ditto 62 dozen sleepers ...' and in January 1759: '... Joyners laying rails in yᵉ East end level ...'. The wagonway system using wooden rails was advancing rapidly and extending into the side workings although the account entries continue to show the limited use of iron or iron-capped rails. Another pioneering development appeared at Coalcleugh at this time, shown in the account entries for April–June 1757: '... Voge wheels Cast Iron from Penrith to Alston is 70 stone @ 3d. per stone—17/6d ....'. Two similar entries closely follow and a year later: '... Math. Brown for carriage of Voge Rail 168 stone—5/– ...', this again implying that some wagon and Vogue ways were either in iron or iron-capped. Sketches in the Science Museum indicate that a Vogue was a two-wheeled wagon similar in size to that of an underground horse-wagon but designed to be pulled by a man.[15] The Coalcleugh clerk's erroneous spelling of the word Vogue suggests that the system was then recently introduced, but it was to spread to the other Blackett mining districts and remain in use for at least 50 years, though limited to selective situations. Whilst appearing occasionally in the mines of some other companies, it was not a method of transport which was generally adopted. Later use of the term 'Vogue Level' on plans does not necessarily mean that they were still being used in that context. That they were introduced at Coalcleugh shortly after Horse Levels could indicate that the miners had appreciated the advantages of wagons over sledges and wheelbarrows, whilst realising that horse transport had its limitations in respect to accessibility and ground conditions. Such levels were most likely designed for areas of the mine above or below day random and where the miners found two-wheeled wagons easier to handle than four. The new system was not extensively used at Coalcleugh, there being only scattered references in the account books. A new vogue drift was begun in 1762 with the same partnership of men driving westwards for 3 years, after which time it disappears from the records. During the course of driving, two 'Vogue Rooms' were cut but few other details are given. References to 'Vogueing' are much more common in the Killhope, Wolfcleugh and Allenheads accounts, particularly the latter, with that method of moving ore and deads coming into increasing use in the period 1770 to 1790 but thereafter rapidly decreasing. The Knopley Vogue Level at Allenheads Mine commenced at a depth of 260 feet in the Gin Hill Whimsey Shaft and was driven at least 1050 yards in an easterly direction, this being one of the longest examples noted. The new technology brought with it a new terminology, some of it related to the costing of the various forms of transport used in and around the mines and the supply of the necessary horse power by the Agents. These officials made a charge for the removal of ore and deads from the mine, some of which was set against the miners earnings. The computed costs for the various functions were listed in the accounts below the individual Agent's salary. The first entry relates to drawing ore or deads along the Horse Level and was calculated in 'shifts' and 'waggons', payment being for 'man with horse'. Up to 1766, eight wagon 'shifts' were common, but in later years six wagon shifts were used. An eight shift wagon contained 30 kibbles, each of 14 quarts, whilst a six shift one contained 40 kibbles. The second entry relates to drawing work from Whimsey Shafts, again by the Agent's man and horse, where the totals are reckoned in Shifts and Kibbles. The large kibbles wound up the shafts were known as 'Horse kibbles' and contained 4 smaller 'Miners (or waggon) kibbles'. Each Whimsey Shift was made up of 60 Horse kibbles. By this system, transport costs were easily calculated whether the work was hauled or wound, or a combination of both. The average rate paid for both functions was 3s. 6d. per shift. The third entry is usually for carrying wood up the level, at 1½d. per wagon, a rate which remained unchanged for fifty years. The next two entries in the Agents lists are more difficult to assess. The fourth is for emptying the wagons, usually at the rate of 4d. per wagon and the fifth entry is for 'Striking Whimsey Kibbles' or 'Striking at the Whimsey', paid for by Shift and Kibble at the rate of 12d. to 14d. per shift. The term 'Strike' is assumed to mean fill, but does not appear in any of the mining dictionaries. On the coalfield 'Strike wood-full' meant filling a container brim-full, but in Cornwall 'Strick' or 'Strike down' meant lowering down a shaft. As Striking and Emptying are consecutively entered in the account books it is presumed to refer to emptying wagons

at the shaft foot and filling the whimsey kibbles for drawing to the surface. It could however relate to unloading kibbles at the surface where the strike boards were, but this seems a less likely interpretation. An associated function was that of 'Hurling', the term first appearing in 1760 and continuing in use to the end of the century. Individuals and partnerships are noted in the accounts '... hurling and striking ... hurling out deads ... hurling at the rail ends ...' which may refer to emptying or throwing out, though indicating the use of a wheelbarrow or 'hurlbarrow' would seem a more likely interpretation. [16] The rate paid for this work was 16d. per shift, suggesting the use of a container of set proportions. During the period under examination and until about 1806, whimsey shaft drawing remains a major itemised function suggesting that larger scale level development was yet to take place. The system which evolved at Coalcleugh spread throughout the whole orefield and continued well into the nineteenth century with most horse power being under the control of the individual Agents. Since much of this transport was paid for by the men in the working partnerships, complaints regarding costs were occasionally made, but no action was ever taken by the Chief Agent, who supported the system. After one such grievance, Erasmus Blackett wrote to Mr Beaumont the proprietor in January 1797: '... as to the charge of the Agent having the advantage of employing some horses I do not see the evil arising from it... and in case they should be deprived of this advantage it will be reasonable that their Salaries should be advanced ...'.[17]

Richard Harrison, the Coalcleugh Senior Agent died in September 1762, but during his eight years in office great changes had taken place. William Hodgson of Alston who took over the Agency at a salary of £50 p.a. died suddenly in the following April. The only major change effected during his short term was the transfer of the Killhope district from the Allenheads agency to Coalcleugh. The Chief Agent wrote to Hodgson: '... as Killhope from its situation falls more naturally under the inspection of your Coalcleugh Agency, Sir Walter has thought it proper to put the mine there under your Management and has appointed Caleb Kidd to be your Assistant at a Salary of £20 a year and he has also appointed Joseph Dickinson to succeed George Armstrong as Under Steward at Coalcleugh at £20 a year provided he will come and live there ...'.

Joseph Richmond the Chief Agent died in April 1763, so the responsibility of finding a new Coalcleugh Agent fell to his son, Henry who succeeded his father. He wrote to Sir Walter in May: '... I find two of the best Grove Stewards in this Country intend to offer their services to you to wit, Mr Brown and Mr Westgarth who are both at present employed under the Quaker Co., but some disagreeable circumstances has made them determined to quit their service if you will accept of them. Mr Brown the Company's Second Agent keeps his intention from them but Mr Westgarth who is Third in rank proceeds more openly ...'. With the London Lead Co.'s agreement William Westgarth took the Coalcleugh Agency in May 1763 at a salary of £60 p.a. and remained there for thirteen years, his responsibilities also covering 'Mohope and Killhope Grooves'. He succeeded to this post at a time when Coalcleugh was the most important and advanced mine within the W. B. Company, it having gone through a decade of remarkable development.

Shortly after his arrival a new Vogue drift to the West began which was to continue for several years, but it was in 1764 that a serious problem arose, the solution to which was to create engineering history and make him famous. In March 1764 the Chief Agent wrote to Sir Walter: '... as to Coalcleugh she was beginning to wear a better face but a feeder of water is broke out in the Great Limestone under the Low Level which was the most hopeful part of the Grove and Mr Westgarth is now struggling with it ...'. At the same time the accounts show a surge of activity with over 100 men involved in pumping water out of the Great Limestone to prevent the new workings below the Low Level from being drowned out. According to Ure's Dictionary water pressure engines had been erected in Germany, Hungary and Saxony between 1748 and 1767 [18] but it is extremely unlikely that William knew anything of these. The hydraulic engine was similar to a steam engine except that it used the pressure of a column of water rather than steam to act upon a plunger in the cylinder. Coalcleugh was an ideal site as it had suitable levels from which to drain the pumped and exhaust water and shafts down which the piped stream of water could be fed to the engine. It was simple, effective and cheap to run. Gabriel Jars, the French mining engineer visited the mine in the early part of 1765 and though he gives a brief description of the principle of the engine, his report implied that it was not yet in operation.[19] John Smeaton, in his representation to the Society of Arts in 1769, promoted his friend William Westgarth's new engine and wrote: '... independently of the various draughts, experiments and essays on models, which I am informed MR WESTGARTH had in hand for years prior to attempting a machine in large, I had the pleasure of seeing the first complete machine of this kind at work for draining or unwatering a lead mine belonging to SIR WALTER BLACKETT at Coalcleugh aforesaid, in the summer of 1765 since which time that machine has been shewn to all those who had the curiosity to see it; he has now erected four others in different mines in the neighbourhood, one of which I have seen, and all attended with great success'.[20] It is clear from the first few lines of this letter that he had been designing the machine for a number of years, a fact born out by information available in the account books. Surprisingly however, no further references to this pioneering work are seen in the letter books of the Company.

The problem with the feeder of water began in early 1764 and in April that year, Westgarth ordered 450 pieces of lead from Allenheads Mill which were made into pipes. Account book entries shortly afterwards state: '... Will. Wilson carrying of lead pipes from Allenheads—266 @ 1/- each ...'. In January– March quarter 1765 '... Will. Millburn for casting etc 35 tons 6 cwts 2 quarters of 5" pipe @ 4/– per cwt—£141-6-0 ...' together with: '... 48 lbs of Solder @ 9d. per lb ... Thomas Robinson, Smithwork for New Engine £1-3-0 ... sundry expenses when fixing the Engine and laying the pipes etc ...'. There is also a list of 46 men: '... letting down lead pipes into the Low Level ...', followed by 6 men: '... cutting a Bob room at levelhead ...' and later in April–June: '... cutting a Capstone room ...' with 4 men on the surface totalling 120 days '... making a Dam...'. The October–December accounts show: '... 57½ lbs of Hoggs Lard for the New Engine, ... 5 men covering lead pipes 240 days @ 12d ... repairing the New

Engine and an engine valve ...'. A Coalcleugh Cash Book records for May 1766 '... By expenses in fixing the new Engine in Killhope—10/6 ...'[21], confirming the Killhope hydraulic engine was in place by that time. There are two earlier entries worth noting, one for 5th April 1764: '... By Cash paid Adam Wilkinson for a Working Barrel for Killhope Engine bought of Mr William Errington—£12-2-0 ...' the other for 5th July 1764: '... By sundry expenses in fixing the Engine at Killhope—£1-5-0 ...', although neither entry qualifies this machinery as 'New' as in previous references. The account books and Smeaton's letter indicate that the first of Westgarth's hydraulic engines was in operation by the summer of 1765. So successful was it that he was requested to construct similar pumping machinery for some of the Nenthead mines worked by the London Lead Company, two engines subsequently being erected in Middlecleugh and one in Rampgill mine. The Lead Company Court of Assistants at their meeting of 3rd September 1767 voted: '... that a Present of 25 Guineas be given to William Westgarth for his new constructed Water Engine in Rampgill Mine ...'.

His engines appear to have been durable, for a visitor to the district in 1793 described his engine at Coalcleugh, then still working and noted that the inventor had been presented with a 'premium' of £50 by the Society of Arts.[22] From the time the water engines were installed two new headings were entered in the accounts, under which 20 or 30 men were often listed: '... Helping to draw spears ...' and '... Helping to Leather the Engines ...'. The pioneering developments taking place at Coalcleugh attracted visitors, some professional like Gabriel Jars who described his excursion in detail in 1765 along the Horse Level to Coalcleugh High Vein and out to the boundary where the workings were linked to those of the London Lead Company in Rampgill Mine. An extract from a layman's description of the same period is perhaps more interesting: '... we went in at the day hole at Colecleugh and travelled about a mile in carriages and then thro' the windings of the mine with infinite difficulty to where Rampgill Mine was working an hundred and five fathoms deep and came up at Nenthead w'ch is ab 2 miles Distant from Colecleugh ...'. He also noted: '... curious machines to pump out the water ...'.[23]

Jonathan and Joseph Hilton, Moormasters of Alston Moor and Tallow Chandlers, were also frequent visitors to these mines, supplying candles. The transfer of information from here to the mines of the London Lead Company and Earl of Carlisle on Alston Moor through their association seems a distinct possibility. Joseph Hilton, by following the accepted Coalcleugh practice of supplying food and drink to the workers was dismissed by the Greenwich Hospital in 1779 when he did the same for the men driving the Nent Force Level at Alston.[24] It is also possible that John Smeaton obtained the idea for this five miles long level, begun by him in 1776, from the innovative developments he had seen at Coalcleugh.

As well as the daily running of a busy mining district, William Westgarth was required to compile and present quarterly and annual accounts to head office, maintain records, organise ore deliveries, take views of the mines and set miners' bargains. Senior Agents also attended the views and bargain settings in other districts, which helped avoid disputes, favouritism or fraud and offered the opportunity for mutual advice. Subsistence money and the annual pay had to be calculated, collected and distributed and anything of importance taking place either within the mines or district as a whole, reported in detail to the Chief Agent in Newcastle. Agent's salaries were meagre but houses or small farms and other facilities were often provided free and there was some encouragement to supplement earnings by providing the horsepower and some materials to the mines under their control. Illness and irregularities were often noted in letters as they were potential hazards to the smooth running of the business. That something was amiss at Coalcleugh is seen in a letter of 4th June 1771, from the Chief Agent, Henry Richmond, to William Westgarth in which he stated: '... I was in hopes that you were better ... but that there may be for the future a less risk of your Health, Sir Walter Blackett is desirous you will engage Mr Westgarth Forster, whom you gave so good a Character of, in his service and is willing to give him £40 a year ...'. The accounts show his appointment as special assistant on the 10th June 1771. William's health deteriorated and in June 1772 he requested and was given leave to go to 'Harrowgate' for treatment, the Chief Agent hoping he would receive '... benefit from the Waters ...'. No details of his illness were given but he was perhaps suffering from some form of arthritis, a condition which would be exacerbated by the cold, damp conditions both inside and outside the mines in that austere environment. After his appointment in June 1771, Westgarth Forster moved from Garrigill to live at Coalcleugh and no doubt gave much needed assistance to his ailing cousin who resided on a small farm at nearby Whiteley Shield. During 1772 and 1773 William Westgarth's health continued to decline and the records show his cousin attending to much of the business, travelling to views and going to meetings with other Agents at Newcastle, assisted by the Second Agent, Joseph Dickinson. No improvement had taken place by 1774, as Henry Richmond wrote in a letter of March that year: '... I am sorry to hear so an indifferent account of your health but I hope it will mend as the Season does—I desire you will take care of yourself and as much as possible of the mines under your care, that you will have as frequent Conferences as your health will permit with Mr Forster, Mr Dickinson and Mr Kidd about the state of the Groves...'.

The impression is given in the available correspondence that whilst his physical health had deteriorated, he remained mentally alert and active. His condition must have worsened as he did not even attend the annual pays in the spring of 1775, these being carried out by Westgarth Forster and Joseph Dickinson on his behalf. Though he was not retired or dismissed, the Company must have realised that he was unlikely to recover and that a replacement would shortly be required. Unfortunately a Principal Agent was also needed to replace Caleb Hunter at Allenheads and the decision was taken to appoint Westgarth Forster and leave Joseph Dickinson to continue at Coalcleugh, with an increase in salary to £40 p.a. and assisted by a new Third Agent, Thomas Crawhall who had been Clerk in Charge at Allenheads Mill. William Westgarth died at his home at Whiteley Shield near Carr Shield on 31st March 1776 and he was buried at the Quaker Meeting House at Wooley Burnfoot near Allendale. All the Newcastle newspapers carried his obituary, that in the *Courant* for Saturday 6th April reading: '... DIED Sunday at Coalcleugh—Mr William Westgarth, one of the people called Quakers, Principal Agent to Sir Walter Blackett's lead mines, well known for his great mechanical genius and particularly for the construction of a Bob Engine to work underground, for which he received the thanks of the Royal Society. He was a sincere friend and an honest man ...'. The *Newcastle Journal* of the same date also carried a 32 line poem to his memory, submitted by Mr JM–D of Weardale, a few lines of which tell of his suffering and fortitude:

> Long near his couch the tyrant took his stand,
> And menac'd oft, and oft withheld his hand,
> Long keen disease and sharp corroding pain,
> Pursu'd the ebbing life from vein to vein,
> But pain ne'er shook him, terror ne'er alarmed,
> By faith supported, and by virtue arm'd.

William Westgarth was succeeded by Joseph Dickinson who remained in the post until 1805, having then served 43 years as a Coalcleugh Agent and by which time that district had ceased to be of primary importance.

The Forster and Westgarth Forster Family.
George Forster, who married Mary the sister of Thomas Westgarth, came from the Whitley Chapel area of Hexhamshire. It is likely that Forster's grandparents were originally from Hexham and were the branch of the family reputed to be connected with the Forsters of Addistone, later to become the Bacon-Forsters of Staward. This early connection was unlikely to have had much, if any, bearing on the later fortunes of the Westgarth Forsters, but that it was through their close links with the Westgarths that the greatest influence came about.

No information has to date been seen to indicate the occupations of George, or his father Edward, who resided at Hole House, Dalton, near Whitley Chapel, although agriculture was, even then, the predominant activity of that district. It is worth noting, however, that this area had a long tradition of lead smelting, with two mills then operating, one at Blackhall about one mile in distance from the family home and the second larger mill at Dukesfield, a short distance beyond. What brought George Forster and Mary Westgarth together is not known. The Westgarths moved to Jeffreys Rake at Hunstanworth, near Blanchland possibly in 1730-1 and were closely connected with the London Lead Co., but whether the Forsters were then also linked with the lead industry has not been ascertained. At the time of their marriage in 1736, Hunstanworth parish registers described them as: '... George Forster of Hexhamshire and Mary Westgarth of Jeffrys Rake ...', suggesting that he was then residing at Dalton. This is supported by the baptism entry of December 1738, in the same register, of their firstborn '... Forrester, Westgarth, Son of George of Dalton ...', although the second son baptised in 1740 was described as: '... George, Son of George of Jeffrys Rake ...'. The fact that the baptisms are in the Hunstanworth register and not that of Slaley or Hexham would indicate that the couple lived at Jeffreys after their marriage, possibly for a time with her family. As the Westgarths were staunch Quakers and the Forsters were not, it is more likely that they met through a common occupational interest, rather than a social or religious one so it still seems feasible that George was connected with lead mining or smelting in the area. He died in December 1753 at Jeffreys Rake after having lived at that place for seventeen years. The only clues to a possible occupation lie in two Lord Crewe Estate rental list entries for 1750–2 which, apart from recording his house rent at £2 10s. 0d., also show on the opposite page under Bills Allowed the entry: '... To Mr. Forsters Surveying and Dividing Nuckton and Shildon—£6/18/0 ...'. A similar entry for the following year shows: '... Paid by Cash—To George Forster—£5/1/0 ...'.[25] These entries suggest that he was a professional man with skills much valued in the mining industry, and this fact linked with his local family connections and his long term residence in this isolated district, would indicate involvement with mining or smelting. If such was the case, then his eldest son Westgarth was brought up and educated in a similar rich industrial environment to his uncle, Thomas Westgarth and family. It is, therefore, not surprising that the two famous cousins were to be closely associated in later life.

The first marriage ceremony of Mary Westgarth and George Forster took place at Hexham on the 26th October 1736, but two days later, on the 28th October, they also celebrated a second marriage at Lamely near Coanwood in the South Tyne Valley. The entry in the Hunstanworth register appears as an abnormal one under the title of '... Marriages Clandistinly at Lamely By Edmund Baxter 1736 ...' and includes a number of other Quaker unions, amongst them Mary's sister Hannah. They resided at Jeffreys Rake close to the mine site, along with many other mining families, including the Westgarths, but whether Jeffreys House, now a crumbled ruin, was ever their home, as often suggested, is not known. Nearby, sunk on the line of the vein, is the capped top of Westgarth's Shaft. Hunstanworth parish registers show the Anglican baptisms of five children, the first being Westgarth on the 17th December 1738, followed by George, John, Hannah, Thomas, and Susannah (who died at birth). George Junior died in 1755 aged 15 years, John in 1761 aged 18, Hannah in 1745 aged 1 year and George Senior, the father, in December 1753 aged 42 years. The family continued to live at Jeffreys Rake after the father's death, Mary's name appearing in the Lord Crewe Estate tenant list covering the period 1757–63.[26] Later information suggests they left the area in 1764–5, although it is not known whether Mary was then still alive, there being no available record of her burial. It is perhaps worth noting that although no Westgarth householders appear in the post-1750 period, grandmother Jane died there in 1751 and a William Westgarth is recorded there in 1753. It is possible that they lived with the Forsters. Of the two remaining Forster children, both Westgarth and Thomas followed careers in mining, that of the former being far more illustrious.

Westgarth Forster married Lucy Emerson, a supposed member of the large Weardale family of that name. There are, however, no records of the birth or baptism of Lucy in any parish registers examined, nor any evidence that she was from a Weardale background. Her epitaph indicates she was born about the year 1743, it initially being conjectured that she was probably from a Quaker family. This view was enhanced when her marriage was traced out of the area to St Margaret's Church

at Durham where the ceremony took place on the 9th June 1766, by special licence. This licence reads: '... 1766 June 9. Forrester Westgarth, Coalcleugh, Allendale, 27 Gent; Emerson, Lucy, St Mary's Durham, 22 ...'. Further research indicated no links with Durham City or the surrounding area, and an examination of many parish registers revealed that Lucy was a very uncommon name at that time, the only recorded entries being in the Alston district. The name Emerson was also found in the same area, particularly around the village of Garrigill, and it was further noted that Thomas Forster had married Mary Emerson in 1772, one of their children being named Lucy. Additional enquiries suggested that Lucy and Mary Emerson were sisters who had married the brothers Westgarth and Thomas Forster. The evidence for Quaker origins diminished, the facts available pointing towards a nonconformist background for the Emerson family, probably as Congregationalists. These independent groups had a strong following in the Alston Moor area, particularly at Garrigill, where early Dissenting Ministers were based. This district was unique in having a separate section of the parish registers for nonconformist births, covering the period 1705–40, after which time the Garrigill and Alston Congregationalists kept their own separate records. Unfortunately, the earliest entries begin in 1763, leaving an unrecorded gap of twenty three years, during which time Lucy and Mary Emerson were born.

The Durham marriage licence reveals that Westgarth Forster was living at Coalcleugh in June 1766, though the Blackett records make no mention of him at that time. It seems most likely that he was staying with his cousin William Westgarth, who was then the resident Senior Agent, but whether he was there for professional or social reasons is not evident, though it was during this period that the hydraulic engines were installed. After their marriage Westgarth and Lucy appear to have taken up residence in Garrigill as Mary, their firstborn, was baptised there in September 1767. The second daughter Susan was born in March 1769, but was not baptised until the 14th April 1771, the same date as the third daughter Lucy, who died four months later. During this period the family were probably living at Ivy House, opposite St John's Church, though no information has yet been seen to indicate how this property was acquired. It may well be that it was an Emerson family holding provided for them after their marriage, and at which they remained until June 1771, after which time they removed to Coalcleugh. They were not to return to their old house until thirty years later in 1801, the property remaining in family hands (later Forster-Brown) until the latter part of the nineteenth century.

It is possible that Thomas Forster came to Garrigill at the same time, perhaps residing with his brother Westgarth. John, the illegitimate son of Thomas Forster and Mary Emerson was baptised at Alston on the 1st. January 1769. The couple were later married at Garrigill in December 1772, and afterwards had at least three more children, of which George, Lucy and Mary are recorded. Thomas was closely involved with mining for much of his life, supplying candles and gunpowder to some of the Blackett mines, as well as attending to ore washing and carriage. He and his son John provided the mine horses at Wolfcleugh for many years, John later residing at that place, after having been trained as a joiner and engineman by his uncle Westgarth. There are indications that Thomas and Mary Forster took up residency of part of the Ivy House estate at Garrigill, some time after it was vacated by Westgarth and Lucy in 1771. Their three legitimate children were baptised at St John's in Garrigill, George in 1773, Lucy in 1774 and Mary in 1776, the latter dying in July 1778. Mary's burial is recorded at Garrigill, the entry referring to her as the daughter of Thomas Forster of Allenheads. This would suggest that their father was by then living at Allenheads and carrying on his candle, tallow, and gunpowder business from there. Mary, his wife, followed him to the village and later ran a public

The Forster family home, Ivy House, Garrigill. Photographed in 1996. *Photograph: Peter Wilkinson.*

house. Thomas died at Allenheads in May 1791, aged 45 years, but was buried at Garrigill next to the main family grave. This side of the family also produced several eminent mining engineers and agents during the nineteenth century, amongst them Thomas Emerson Forster and his son George Baker Forster.

Up to the time of Westgarth Forster's removal to Coalcleugh in June 1771, little is known of his professional career, though it must be assumed that he was experienced in mining matters and had been employed in some branch of the industry, otherwise he would not have been requested as an assistant by his ailing cousin, William Westgarth. Westgarth Forster Junior was born at Coalcleugh in 1772, but was baptised at St Augustine's Church at Alston on the 8th December 1772. It is now uncertain why he was not baptised in his home parish at West Allendale. Westgarth Forster Senior remained at Coalcleugh until mid-1775 and it is possible that his son George was born there, though no record of his baptism has yet been found. Little is known of George's life, and he is last noted at Carlisle in 1825. Phoebe, the fourth daughter, was baptised at Allenheads in May 1778, where her father had been Principal Agent since 1775. She married Thomas Brown of Garrigill in October 1806 and is remembered for her small book 'The Garrigill Poachers', which was published at Alston in 1819. Phoebe died at Garrigill on the 11th November 1836, aged 58 years and was buried in the family grave. Of the third son, William, little is recorded other than a note of his mother giving him £18 to go to London when he was 18 years old.[27] He died there in 1812, aged 32 years, the details being inscribed on the family gravestone in St John's churchyard. Westgarth Forster Senior removed from Allenheads in July 1795, taking up residence at Unthank, Stanhope in Weardale, where he became involved in farming. He died shortly afterwards in February 1797 aged 59 years, and was buried at Garrigill. His

widow Lucy appears to have vacated Unthank in about 1801 and returned to Ivy House at Garrigill, where she died in September 1806, aged 63 years, being buried beside her husband. The Forster-Browns later lived at Ivy House, the family producing a succession of distinguished Mining Agents and Inspectors, the last still practising in the 1950s.

Westgarth Forster—Father & Son.
It is proposed to examine the careers of the Westgarth Forsters in more detail, making use of the Blackett Lead Company archive and in particular the Allenheads and Coalcleugh Quarterly Accounts, together with the Chief Agent's Letter Books. Westgarth Forster Senior is shown to have been at Coalcleugh in 1766, yet there is no confirmation that he was then involved in mining business with his cousin William Westgarth, although this seems likely during that busy 'engine' period. By the time he was officially employed on the 10th June 1771, the Coalcleugh mines had been developed and expanded under a series of innovative agents, making full use of the latest technology. There were well established horse levels with underground wagonways, a long drainage level, vogueways, large whimsey shafts, hydraulic and other pumping engines, excellent plans and geological sections, much improved accounts and reports, and a new terminology to go with the new working methods. Underground and surface surveying was well established with regular orders for plane-tables, surveyor's chains, dialling equipment and compass needles being seen in the accounts. Forster was put into a unique elevated position on his arrival as Assistant to the Principal Agent, which suggests that he was already an accomplished miner. He obviously held a position of seniority over the Second Agent, Joseph Dickinson, as his introductory salary was £40 per annum, twice that of the latter. The ailing William Westgarth was recommended to take on a suitable assistant to ease the burden of his duties by Sir Walter Blackett himself.

That both William and his cousin Westgarth Forster were held in high regard by the then Chief Agent, Henry Richmond, is demonstrated by the tone of his many letters to them. As William's health declined, Westgarth took over more of his general duties, as well as attending meetings and assisting with views and bargain letting at Allenheads. He also took some responsibility for the Killhope mines, which had been part of the Coalcleugh district since 1763, supported by the sub agent there, Caleb Kidd. In William Westgarth's absence, instructions for control of the mines in the Coalcleugh area were directed to Mr W. Forster, J. Dickinson and C. Kidd in that order of seniority. It is notable that in his four years based there, Westgarth Forster had little involvement in the horse drawing or supply of materials, this remaining in the hands of the Principal and Second Agents.

During 1775 Caleb Hunter, the Principal Agent at Allenheads became ill and a replacement was urgently needed. Richard Allgood the Second Agent there, whilst very dependable, was old and nearing retirement and the Third Agent, Robert Allgood his son, was unreliable. At Coalcleugh William Westgarth's health was deteriorating, and it was apparent he would never return to full time duties. The decision was taken to appoint Forster to Allenheads to replace Caleb Hunter, with Joseph Dickinson promoted to cover William's position at Coalcleugh. Dickinson's salary was raised to £40 per annum, and a Third Agent, Thomas Crawhall, was appointed to assist him, being transferred from Allenheads Smelt Mill. These rearrangements took place at the end of June 1775, with Westgarth Forster installed at Allenheads for the start of the July–September quarter at a salary of £60 per annum. William Westgarth died on the 31st March 1776, and his place as Senior Agent was taken, as planned, by Joseph Dickinson, with Crawhall moving up into the Second Agent's post.

Allenheads Period.
The new volume of accounts which begin with Westgarth Forster's Allenheads agency note at an early date payments for '… Mr. Westgarth Forster's man and horse …' which indicates that he had begun horse drawing, a business he was to develop and later involve other members of the family. Shortly after his arrival there were several letters concerning the dismissal of the Third Agent, Robert Allgood, who left in December 1775 and was immediately replaced, upon the orders of Sir. Walter, by Lancelot Allgood. This agent only remained in place until October 1777, after which time the post was filled by Thomas Westgarth at a salary of £25 per annum. In September 1777 the old and very reliable Richard Allgood was retired and pensioned off, with a new Second Agent, James Mulcaster, put in his place at a salary of £30 per annum.

Within a year of his appointment as Principal Agent, Forster had begun a major new scheme upon which much of the later development of the mine was to rely. The Fawside Level was commenced in 1776 (the same year as the Nent Force Level at Alston) and was designed as a horse level with wagonway. The project was similar to those at Coalcleugh, but it is unlikely that he could have appreciated how essential it would be to the mine's long term success. This drift, with the High and Low Underground Shafts to which it was connected, became one of the vital arteries of the mine. In about 1851 two of Sir William

Armstrong's hydraulic engines were built in chambers at the head of these shafts, which facilitated much of the later successful working of the lower strata, remaining in operation until closure in 1896. After his visit to Allenheads in 1793 the Rev. William Turner wrote: '… we were conducted by Mr. Forster Junior in waggons drawn upon a regular waggonway, to the extremity of Fawside Level… for upwards of a mile and a half in a South East direction … out of Northumberland and into the County of Durham …'.[28] Matthew Rowell began driving the level at 35s. per fathom and he and his family were associated with work on the project up to the time of the Revd Turner's visit, the price of driving being occasionally as high as 70s. per fathom. Forster's man and horse were drawing out waste and ore from the commencement of driving, the usual rate for this work being 3s. 6d. per shift of six wagons. Major changes in the W. B. Lead Company took place in 1777. A Weardale bargain book records: '… Be it remembered that Sir Walter Blackett, Bart. departed this Life on the 14th of February 1777 at 10 at night …'.[29] He had been involved with the mines for fifty years and was in regular contact with his staff, particularly the Chief Agent in Newcastle, so his death had noticeable repercussions. The Company passed into the hands of a stranger to the concern, Sir Thomas Wentworth of Bretton near Wakefield, who later took the name of Blackett. Another event took place at this time that had an even more dramatic effect on the smooth running of the Company and resulted in a period of uncertainty. The Chief Agent, Henry Richmond, who had been ailing for some years, died and was replaced by John Erasmus Blackett. Initially the relationship between Forster and Erasmus Blackett appears to have been an amicable one, but the letter books demonstrate the Chief Agent's increasing dissatisfaction with the way the Allenheads district was run. The situation was perhaps exacerbated by the fact that Forster was well respected and had the support of Sir Thomas to whom he made direct requests on various matters without consulting the Chief Agent. The year 1786 seems to have marked the turning point in the relationship between Westgarth Forster and the Chief Agent, the situation no doubt aggravated by a number of Company and personal problems. In January 1786 Erasmus wrote to Sir Walter, '… I have been confined to the house with a violent rheumatic complaint in my back. I am still very lame …'.[30] His letter continues: '… The late floods have done a great deal of damage at Allenheads, the river changing its course … filled the present workings so suddenly that it was with great difficulty that 8 men were saved … will lay off the works for near 3 months …'. At the same time James Mulcaster retired as Second Agent with an annuity of £10 per annum, his place being taken by the Third Agent, Thomas Westgarth, leaving that position vacant. Shortly afterwards this post was filled by Westgarth Forster Junior, then still only thirteen years old, at a salary of £20 per annum. It can only be assumed that the appointment was not with the sanction of the Chief Agent, particularly as the mine was in a state of some crisis at the time. How young Westgarth had been educated up to this point is not known, although it is probable that he was schooled by his parents, for to reach the necessary degree of competence to fill an Assistant District Agent's post, it is likely that he had been working with his father since childhood. At the same time, Mr Salkeld, assistant to the Senior

Smelting Agent Isaac Hunter at Dukesfield, had had a serious stroke, and William Westgarth Junior (the second cousin of Westgarth Forster Junior) was recommended for his position; he was 23 years old and described as: '... honest, sober and diligent...'.

Allenheads mines showed a loss of £1,769 in 1786, some of the deficiency being due to the effects of the recent flood. At the same time, the Coalcleugh area showed a profit of £5,889 and Weardale, which was then rising to a position of predominance in the concern, a gain of £10,691. Little improvement was seen the following year at Allendale with the loss reduced to £909, although profits at Coalcleugh jumped to £9,095, with Weardale returning a massive £16,306 gain. The total Blackett Lead Company profits for the year 1787 were a record £27,000, much of the increase being due to the prevailing high price of lead.[31] During this period, Allenheads district was subject to close scrutiny. It was noted that a total of £4,178 had been expended in the land account for the nine year period 1777–85, and the Chief Agent remarked in a letter of March 1787 to Sir Thomas Blackett: '... Mr. Westgarth Forster has expended a considerable sum this year in repairs and walling—£630/4/7, which is double the Rent of the Estate. It is high time he held his hand ...'.[32] Talks were held with Forster at which Erasmus '... convinced him of his erroneous calculations ...' and Forster promised '... to exert himself ...'.

In October 1787 there is a long letter to Sir Thomas regarding the supply of candles and other materials to the mines. Erasmus Blackett wanted Joshua Straker to have a share in supplying the candles to the company mines, his letter stating that, '... In part of the time of Sir Walter Blackett, Frauds and Irregularities arose from the Mine Agents furnishing Articles to the Mines and it was found necessary to put a stop to that evil, since which it has been a standing rule in the Concern ... that no Lead Mine Agent shall furnish the mines with any one article, however as you are pleased to direct that Mr. Westgarth Forster's Son is to supply the mines with Candles, I beg ... you will please to allow Mr. Joshua Straker to have a part of the business ... by which means there will be an amelioration between them as which shall furnish Candles of the best quality ...'.[33] Shortly afterwards, in June 1788, George Forster is recorded in the Accounts Journals as supplying both Allenheads and Wolfcleugh mines with candles and at a later date those at Coalcleugh, continuing to provide this service until December 1801. It would appear from the tone of the letter that the Forsters had made a direct arrangement with Sir Thomas, rather than with the Chief Agent, as would be expected. During the period 1787–95, the accounts show entries for both candles and gunpowder under the agents salaries, which would suggest they were controlling sales. A typical entry, here for October–December 1787 shows: '... Candles on wages 108 doz. 6lbs @ 8/-, £43/8/0. Gunpowder on wages 52lbs @ 13d, £2/16/4 ...'.[34]

There are clear indications that Westgarth Senior's brother Thomas, was a long term supplier of materials and services to the mines, particularly at Wolfcleugh in the Rookhope Valley. This Weardale mine was controlled by Forster, a duty he carried out without remuneration, as is seen by a letter of November 1794 to Erasmus Blackett in which he states '... I

never had one sixpence for Directing the Works at Wolfcleugh, but gave up the Horses so as to have a person that I could confide in constantly upon the place ...'. The same letter also notes that his nephew John and brother Thomas, '... delivered the Gunpowder and Candles there for this 19 years and looked to the Washing and Delivery of the Ore ...'.[35] Westgarth Senior kept a detailed Wolfcleugh Account Book for the period 1777–86 which shows regular payments to Thomas for horsework and carriage, both above and below ground. It has been previously noted that such work was usually under the Agent's control, but here Forster had his brother and nephew on site for much of the time at no salaried cost to the Company. As the mines developed and horse-work opportunities increased, so did the earnings of those Agents involved. In addition to drawing and carrying, they also often controlled and were paid for associated tasks such as hurling, filling and emptying. By the turn of the century, the amounts involved were very substantial, Joseph Little, for example, the senior agent at Coalcleugh in 1807, being paid £563 for this work. The miners Bargains included many of these costs and in addition usually had the expense of buying candles and gunpowder, either from the Agents or external suppliers. With regard to mine supplies in general, the Chief Agent stated in 1794: '... we have always thought it advisable to divide the business amongst a few of the principal dealers in the several articles for the mines, as it serves to keep up some kind of competition ...'.[36] In early August 1788 Thomas Westgarth, the Second Agent at Allenheads, died and the Chief Agent wrote to Sir Thomas: '... I hope that a skilful, sober person, may be met with to succeed him ... for Forster's Son is certainly too young for 2nd Agent and Archer the Woodman (who has assisted since the illness of Thomas Westgarth) is not equal to the charge ...', the latter point referring to Archer taking the Third Agent's place.[37] Forster Senior had proposed these two successors, but was told by the Chief Agent that their appointment was out of the question. He must have privately petitioned Sir Thomas, however, as Erasmus Blackett was overruled and Westgarth Forster Junior was installed as Second Agent at the age of sixteen at a salary of £40 per annum. Forster Senior went further and installed Thomas Archer as Third Agent on a salary of £30 per annum. The new agents must have applied themselves as the situation at Allenheads improved, the letter books later only displaying routine business.

By late 1794, the available records indicate that Westgarth Senior was unhappy with his situation and was intending to resign his post at Allenheads. His relationship with Erasmus Blackett had deteriorated and criticisms of his work became more frequent in the Chief Agent's letters. In December 1794 there was severe unrest in the lead districts with the miners complaining about the high cost of rye and about this time '... papers were fixed at Allenheads ... of a Riotous and Seditious tendency ...', Forster neglecting to inform the Chief Agent of this. Erasmus Blackett wrote to Colonel Beaumont about the matter, adding: '... Forster Senior ... has taken a large farm and intends giving up his employment at Allenheads, in which he is in hopes of his Son succeeding him, but in my opinion he is not equal to the Trust and I have other objections to him ...'.[38] In January 1795 Colonel Beaumont wanted to relieve the miners of their paying 5/- each per year in support of the local clergy, a move which Erasmus vigorously objected to, seeing it as an increase in wages. In his letter of disapproval to the Colonel he wrote: '... I never heard the men make the least complaint until Mr. Forster put it into their heads ...'.[39] The Chief Agent wrote to Joseph Dickinson at Coalcleugh in February 1795 ordering him to send his Second Agent, Thomas Crawhall, to check on the validity of a report of '... a rich grove discovered at Allenheads ...' and seemed quite incensed that the discovery had not been communicated to him by the Forsters.[40]

Whether pressure of work, the enmity of Erasmus Blackett, or general disenchantment with the new regime prompted Forster's change of profession is not known, but at the end of June 1795 he vacated his Principal Agent's post as planned. He and other family members took up residence on the Unthank estate at Stanhope, which was previously the home of the Weardale Westgarths. No evidence has been seen of any relationships between these two family groups. John Westgarth, the last of the male line, had died at Unthank in 1781, leaving the estate in the hands of his three daughters and it appears that the Westgarth Forsters leased the Hall and farm from one of these. When Forster Senior left Allenheads he had settled neither his business nor personal affairs and his relationship with Erasmus Blackett was to further deteriorate. When an Agent resigned or died all business moneys had to be accounted for and the books balanced. This procedure was not finalised in Forster's case, leaving the family with substantial debts to settle, for Mr Straker and Mr Bell of Hexham the Surveyor and Land Agent, had examined the Allenheads mine and rental accounts and found them to be incomplete, although the inventory of house contents was proved to be correct. The Chief Agent's letters to Colonel and Mrs Beaumont were critical of the latter period of Forster's agency and demonstrate an attempt to denigrate the Senior Agent's name, making sure that other members of the family were removed from positions of influence in the Allenheads area.

In a very long letter of the 24th September 1795 to Colonel Beaumont, Erasmus Blackett gives a full account of his final arrangements for that district. Thomas Crawhall, the Second Agent at Coalcleugh, was to have the Allenheads Principal Agent's post at a salary of £60 per annum and move into Forster's old house, and his son, referred to as '... a sober and well qualified young man ...', was to replace Joseph Archer as the Third Agent. Archer was again described as: '... never fit for the job ...' and was to go back to being a Woodman. Westgarth Forster Junior was to be removed from his Second Agent's post and transferred to Coalcleugh as Second Agent under Joseph Dickinson at a salary of £45 per annum. The latter move seemed surprising, as Forster had been an Allenheads agent since he was 13 and was then a mature and very experienced 23 year old. Blackett's letter also noted that the Second Agent's residence had been renovated and extended by Forster Senior and turned into a Public House which he let to his brother Thomas, the candle and horsework supplier, whilst at the same time allowing the official Ale House, run by Nicholson the Engineman, to be neglected and fall into disrepair. He suggested that the rule of only allowing one Public House in Allenheads had been broken, '... with very bad consequences not only to the Concern, but to the Health and

Morals of the Workmen ...'.[41] adding that the widow Mary Forster should agree to be removed by August 1796 when her licence expired, at which time the new Second Agent would move into the property. This situation must have existed for some years, as Thomas died in May 1791, from which time Mary had continued the business. Her name appears in the accounts for supplying ale up to the time of her agreed departure. Westgarth Junior, who was unmarried, had held the position of Second Agent since October 1788 and it is assumed that he still lived with his parents. His official residence (a house and small farm) was therefore empty and free for conversion to a hostelry.

Despite many requests, Westgarth Forster Senior had still not paid his outstanding debts to the Company by the end of 1796, nearly a year and a half after leaving his employment at Allenheads. A letter sent to him at Unthank by the Chief Agent dated 1st December 1796 stated: '... you have not paid the Balance of your Account ... likewise the money that you have in your hands belonging to the Club at Allenheads, according to your Promise ...'. If not paid by Christmas Day, he was informed '... measures will be taken to enforce the Payment ...'.[42] On the 30th January 1797, Mr Bell the land agent at Hexham, was contacted by Erasmus Blackett and asked if he had yet obtained security for the outstanding debt and if not, to do so immediately, as Forster was dangerously ill. It appears from this and subsequent letters that Westgarth Senior had given Bell the authority to advertise a small estate he owned to raise the money, but had not signed any bond for the debt. The advert which appeared in both the *Newcastle Courant* and *Chronicle* for Saturday January 28th and February 4th 1797, was for the Ivy Estate at Garrigill on Alston Moor, which was divided into two farms, each with house, byre and stable and respectively known as High and Low Ivy. Forster died on the 1st of February after a short illness, in the midst of urgent efforts to obtain some form of security from him. He was buried in St John's churchyard at Garrigill on the 4th February, his being the first entry on the large family gravestone. Several obituaries appeared in the Newcastle newspapers, that in the *Chronicle* of Saturday February 4th 1797 reading, 'DIED—Wed. At Unthank, in his 59th year, Mr. Westgarth Forster: esteemed for his general worth, and one of the best judges of lead mines in the North of England.'

In the knowledge that the widow was both Executor and the principal beneficiary of the will, Erasmus Blackett vigorously pursued the debt and in March 1797 proposed that: '... Mrs Forster and her sons join in a security for the debt and on refusal to bring an action against her, the Executor ...'.[43] There was confusion regarding the amount of debts involved, particularly with regard to the Club money (possibly the Loyal Miners Club of Allenheads?), the accounts suggesting that he had spent £300 more than he had received! Lucy Forster eventually agreed: '... to pay £200 in May next and give security for the payment of the remainder in 1 year from that time at two payments ...'.[44] The last available letter, dated 6th January 1798, was from Mrs Forster stating: '... I made a sale of my Stock and Property on the 14th September last but was obliged to give six months credit, so it will be about Ladyday before I get my money, but you may depend on my coming to Newcastle at that time, in order to discharge a part of the

Bond …'.[45] This note in her own hand is polite, well structured and beautifully written, suggesting an educated background. The details of the outcome of this unhappy affair are to be found in the comprehensive Account Journals. About a month after Ladyday 1798, Lucy Forster paid £204. 12*s*. 0*d*. '… on account of her Bond … for the Arrears of her late Husband …', with the final instalment of £76. 8*s*. 7¾*d*., to settle the debt, being made on the 11 October 1802, nearly six years after his death.[46]

The Revd Nall had access to some of the family papers, amongst them being Mrs Forster's 'Memorandum Book of Cash Paid and Received by her after the Death of her Husband in 1797, at Unthank and Garrigill'. It was a meticulous record of all moneys received and expended over an eight year period, the first entry being on the 14th January 1797, supposedly the day her husband became ill and the last on the 3rd May 1806, four months before her death. Keeping such a careful record no doubt greatly assisted her in eventually settling her late husband's affairs. Nall also examined family letters, from which he concluded that Lucy gave up the Unthank leases at Stanhope and later removed to Garrigill in about 1801, continuing to live with her family in the unsold portion of the Ivy Estate until her death in September 1806, aged 63 years. She was buried alongside her husband in the churchyard opposite Ivy House.

Westgarth Forster Junior.

There is little factual detailed information on Westgarth Forster Junior's earlier life and much of that which has been previously published is of a conjectural nature. The Revd W. Nall in his Memoir of Forster and his family which is contained in the third edition of *A Section of the Strata* (1883) gives a much more accurate account of his life in the post 1809 period, based on a large collection of letters, plans and other documents to which he was given access

The Forster family grave in St John's churchyard, Garrigill with Ivy House in the background. Photographed in 1996   *Photograph: Peter Wilkinson.*

by the family. The bulk of this material has not been traced, but Nall's manuscript notes, together with oddments of original documents, have been examined in detail and whilst they give a satisfactory overview of his later life, still provide little information about his early years.

Nall examined a large copy book and other documents kept by Westgarth Junior when a boy of about fourteen, which illustrated his abilities in surveying and drawing plans and sketches, all of which were executed in a neat and precise manner. Forster was then the Third Agent of the Allenheads mining district, carrying out his duties under the supervision of

his father. By the time he was sixteen he had been promoted to Second Agent, a position of even greater responsibility, for during his father's occasional absences he was in charge of all operations within that area. He retained that post for a period of seven years from October 1788 to June 1795. Erasmus Blackett, in 1795, had judged Joseph Archer to have been a doubtful choice as Third Agent, but he did not dispute Forster's capabilities as Under Agent and moved him to an equivalent position at Coalcleugh with a higher salary. His father possibly jeopardised any further promotion by leaving his own post with unbalanced books and outstanding debts.

As there are no letter books extant for the period 1800–09, Westgarth Forster Junior's career during those years can only be briefly plotted through entries in the Coalcleugh account books. More importantly, there are no opportunities to examine the reorganisation of 1805, in which he was removed from his post and his services dispensed with. The accounts show that Forster Junior brought his horses with him from Allenheads, as entries appear immediately for drawing whimsey work. In 1801, for example, Forster was paid £92 for his horsework. There are no details regarding the specific nature of his work at that time, the only available records being the Quarterly Accounts. It seems likely, however, that he was spending an increasing amount of time on his geological research, as there are in existence a number of cross sections and notes for that period, which are not related to his area of employment.

In about 1801 his mother and remaining family moved from Unthank in Weardale back to the small unsold portion of the Ivy Estate at Garrigill, at which time she had still not settled her late husbands debt to Col. Beaumont under the agreed Bond. It would seem that Westgarth's salary was more than sufficient for his needs, as he paid a regular sum to his mother. As he was unmarried and lived in a free company property in an isolated area, his outgoings were no doubt slight. His mother Lucy's Account Book showed that he paid her 11 guineas in 1799, £26 in 1800 and similar payments each year thereafter up to 1805, the time he left his agency post.[47] In March 1802 Thomas Dickinson the Third Agent, was replaced by the Senior Agent's son, Joseph Dickinson Junior, at a salary of £40 per annum, but he was only to remain in place until the reorganisation in June 1805.

The days of the old regime were numbered, with the removal of Erasmus Blackett as Chief Agent in December 1804. He was replaced by a relative, Christopher Blackett, who completely restructured the organisation. A record of all the proposed changes, with job descriptions, are given in a manuscript in the company archive, dated January 1805, put together by James Cockshutt and Charles Brown.[48] The report stated: '... The Principal Agent at each of the three Mines (districts) to have the privilege of employing Horses to draw all the Lead Ore, Bouse Ore, Dead Work, etc. from their respective Mines, also for the Carriage of Timber or other Materials ...'.[49] The Chief Agent, Christopher Blackett, was instructed to put the new scheme into operation, making the necessary arrangements: '... as soon as can conveniently and with propriety be done ...'. It is worth noting that great attention was paid to the keeping of full plans of the mine workings, together with written reports and projections of future work, all ideas originally carried out and promoted by the Westgarth Forsters.

Under the reorganisation, all three Coalcleugh agents were replaced, Joseph Dickinson Senior was retired and both Westgarth Forster and Joseph Dickinson Junior, were 'discontinued.' The Dickinsons were paid up to Midsummer, but Forster's salary was terminated on the 30th April 1805. The accounts show three new agents installed on the 1st May, with a fourth being added in October and a fifth the following year in October 1806, though no job designations were noted. The new Principal Agent was Joseph Little on a much improved salary of £100 per annum with complete control, under the new regulations, of all horsework and carriage.

The reasons for Westgarth Forster's removal are not recorded, nor why an alternative post was not found for him. That his services were discontinued may suggest that he did not fit into the new categories of agents who specialised in a particular department. With Mr Dickinson's retirement at that time, it is surprising that he was not offered the post of Principal Agent, for which he was surely well qualified, with twenty years of agency experience and yet still being only 33 years old. It may have been his own decision to leave the W. B. Lead Co. and to pursue his own interests, particularly his geological research. Fragments of information from several sources describe him as a shy, retiring man of somewhat eccentric habits, with a kind and gentle disposition. He was also variously noted as being studious and at times absent-minded, a rather remarkable man, well dressed and of smart appearance, but wearing his hair long. Such descriptions, combined with previous accounts of his work from that period infer that he had become more of an academic and although 'remarkable' and 'ingenious', was not, therefore, the ideal candidate for a mine agent within the more fixed regime which was planned.

Although no information has been seen regarding Forster's movements or activities during the 1805–09 period, it is assumed he returned to the family home at Garrigill after leaving Coalcleugh. His mother Lucy and sisters Phoebe and Susan were then living at Ivy House farm. Lucy died in September 1806 and Phoebe married Thomas Brown the following month, leaving Westgarth in residence with his sister Susan. It is not now known whether he was involved in any mining activity or consultancy work at that time, though the small legacy from his mother and income from the farm probably provided enough means to support himself and his sister.

When his 158 page book *A Treatise on a Section of the Strata* was published in 1809, amongst the list of 181 subscribers were all the agents of the W. B. Lead Co., including the new Chief Agent and Christopher Blackett, as well as Colonel Beaumont, who took six copies. An undated advertisement concerning a further volume entitled A Survey of the Mining District provided with the Treatise, gave some clues as to his other activities whilst based at Garrigill. He was selling 'Numbered specimens of the Strata, or Lead Measures, accompanied with an Engraved Section, Price £2/2/0 per set, Also Cabinet Specimens, which occur in the Mines in Alston Moor, etc., properly classed'.[50] This gives some indication of the advanced knowledge and techniques which he then possessed and was actively promoting to both amateur and professional alike. Other services he then offered were, 'Mines Surveyed and Planned with Accuracy', and 'Young Gentlemen instructed in Subterraneous Surveying, etc.' After the publication of his book, great changes, both personal and professional took place in Forster's life and he embarked upon a new career as consulting mine agent and surveyor, a profession that was to take him to many parts of the world and out of permanent residence at Garrigill on Alston Moor.

References.

1. Obituary in *Newcastle Courant* Sat 6th April 1776. Also *Newcastle Journal* and *Newcastle Weekly Chronicle*
2. IAN FORBES pers. comm. Nov. 1995. List and information on some early Quakers.
3. CAINE, CAESAR. *Register of St John's Garrigill 1699–1730.* Edited entries and notes (1901).
4. NRO 452/E2 (1–12). Lord Crewe Estate, Rental Lists 1729–85.
5. NALL, WM. MSS. Copy notes from *An Account of the Affairs of the Gov. & Co.* etc.
6. *Ibid.*
7. As before (2).
8. WESTGARTH, THOMAS. Volume of Miscellaneous Plans and Reports. (1740–2), Private source.

9. NRO 672/2/50, W. B. Lead Co. Chief Agent's Letter Books.

10. NRO 672/2/47–50, W. B. Lead Co. Chief Agent's Letter Books.

    NRO 672/2/98–101, Coalcleugh Quarterly Accounts.

11. DICKINSON, J & DICKINSON, T, Alston Mines, Report (1821).

12. SOPWITH, THOMAS *An Account of the Mining Districts of Alston Moor* etc (1833), 119

13. ASHTON, T.S. AND SYKES, J. *The Coal Industry of the Eighteenth Century* (1929), 62.

14. GALLOWAY, R.L. *Annals of Coal Mining*, etc. 1st. Ed. (1898).

15. Lead Mining Sketches—Pictorial Archives Dept., Science Museum, London. *Circa* 1805–20. Item No. 17.

16. Suggested by Ian Forbes, pers. comm. see also HESLOP, REVD O. *Northumberland Words*, etc 1892. Hurl = Horl; Horl = to trundle, wheel or whirl; Horl-barra = Wheelbarrow.

17. NRO 672/2/50, W. B. Lead Co. Chief Agent's Letter Books.

18. Ure's *Dictionary of Arts, Manufactures and Mines*. (1863), 851.

19. JARS, GABRIEL, *Voyages Metallurgiques* (1774–81), Vol.2, Section II, 536–45, Rampgill and Coalcleugh Mines.

20. SMEATON, J. Letter and Report to Soc. of Arts 1769. Also *Reports of John Smeaton*, 1st Ed. (1812), 376; 2nd Ed. (1842), 96.

21. NRO 672/2/86 Coalcleugh District Cash Book 1763–1836.

22. TURNER, REVD WM. *An Account of a Short Tour Through the Lead Mine Districts*. (Read September 1793). In: *Trans. Lit & Phil. Soc. Newcastle*. Vol. 1 Pt. 1 (1831).

23. NRO. Document found by Dr S. M. Linsley in the Swinburne papers and quoted in *Off the Record*.

24. WILKINSON, P & HELLIWELL, J, 'The Nent Force Level' in *Men, Mines & Minerals* (1992), 85–93.

25. NRO 452/E2 (1–12) Lord Crewe Estate—Rental Lists etc. 1729–85.

26. *Ibid.*

27. Lucy Forster's Memorandum Book—entry 4 December 1798 noted in Nall's memoir, Third ed. of *A Section of the Strata* (1883).

28. TURNER, REVD WM. *An Account of a Short Tour* etc. (1793).

29. NRO 672/2/67 Breckonsike Bargain Book 1760–90.

30. NRO 672/2/50, W. B. Lead Co. Chief Agent's Letter Books.

31. Figures from profit sheets in NRO ZBL 212 Correspondence of J. E. Blackett.

32. NRO 672/2/50, W. B. Lead Co. Chief Agent's Letter Books.

33. *Ibid.*

34. NRO 672/2/71 Allenheads Quarterly Accounts.

35–37. NRO ZBL 209 Letters to J. E. Blackett.

38–44. NRO 672/2/50, W. B. Lead Co. Chief Agent's Letter Books.

45. NRO ZBL 226 Corr. of J. E. Blackett.

46. NRO 672/2/23 W.B.Lead Co. Account Journal.

47. NALL, WM., MSS.—notes in collection.

48. NRO (Unclassified documents)—Blackett of Wylam Papers – January 1805.

49. *Ibid.*

50. Advertisement sheet. Undated. In private collection.

Acknowledgements
 Grateful thanks to:

John Helliwell for all his help with research, editing and typing.

Andrew Helliwell for checking and word processing.

Northumberland Record Offices at Gosforth & Morpeth.

Newcastle-upon-Tyne City Library.

Cumbria Record Office at Carlisle.

Ian Forbes of Killhope Lead Mining Centre for comments and information.

Rachel Etheridge for research and assistance.

The Quarry Industry in Teesdale

Harold L. Beadle

To become conversant with the quarry industry in Teesdale a brief reference to the origin of the rocks will help the reader to understand more clearly how the different types were quarried and used. The sandstones and limestones are sedimentary rocks which were formed during the carboniferous period, and are often referred to as the Carboniferous Succession, which means that there is a succession of beds of limestone, shale and sandstone which outcrop in many places along the sides of the valley giving easy access for working.

Later, about the end of the carboniferous period, there was added an intrusive rock known as the Great Whin Sill which can be seen outcropping on the south-west side of the valley, almost all the way from Middleton-in-Teesdale to Green Hurth near to the Cumbrian border. The outcrop of this rock in Holwick, Dine Holme, Cronkley Scar and Falcon Clints is spectacular. It is on that side of the valley that the largest whinstone quarries can be seen. Then there are three basaltic dykes to be considered. Namely, the Hett, Cleveland and Lunedale Dykes which have made their contribution mainly in the early days of the quarrying of igneous rocks.

Later still, during a period of glaciation when the valley was formed, there was revealed rock of Ordovician age often referred to as being the Skiddaw Slates which play a small part.

No date can be given for the beginning of the use of stone for the various purposes such as house building, field walls and road making, etc. Innumerable places can be seen where the outcrops have been worked. In Upper Teesdale many of these are not in the lower parts of the valley, but high up on the fells. This relates, in particular, to the sandstones which in many places gave abundant supplies of good quality building stone, flags and slates. Places such as Holwick Fell, Gate Castles, Carr Crags, Church Bowers, Harthope Fell and Knotted Scar. Below Middleton-in-Teesdale, for well-known geological reasons, the quarries can be found in varying locations which include Bail Hill, Windy Hill, Shipley, Stainton, Cat Castle and Dunn House. With the exception of Windy Hill, which is of recent date, it is from these quarries that many of the buildings in the nearby villages and the town of Barnard Castle have been built. Sandstone over a great number of years has proved to be the most popular for building because many of the deposits can be classed as being freestone which dresses more easily than limestone, which was in any case avoided in house building because it was prone to damp. Some of the sandstones qualify as ganister and have been quarried and used in the manufacture of high grade refractory bricks.

Limestone until the 1920s was the most popular stone for road making. It was often adjacent to the roads where it was to be used, easy to quarry and break down, and when the road surfaces were water-bound limestone broken down to two inches in size proved to be more suitable than either sandstone or whinstone because of its better binding qualities.

Limestone was also burnt to produce lime which was used mainly for application to the land in order to neutralise the high acid content of the soil, for building and whitewashing the houses. It was applied each year in order to damp-proof the walls until the 1939–45 war when the Raby Estates decided it should be done every two years. In times past a small amount was used in the lead smelting processes and within living memory both limestone and lime were supplied to the iron and steel works on Teesside for use as a flux in iron smelting.

Little whinstone was quarried until about 1870. Doubtless there was some obtained from the outcrops which, as has already been indicated are extensive. But whinstone, being a very hard rock, was not to be won as easily as sandstone and limestone, so its early use seems to have been limited to areas where it was immediately available. Holwick, which is overshadowed by the sill, is a good example of where it has been used in the field walls and in some of the house and farm buildings. It was the coming of the railway to Middleton-in-Teesdale in 1868 which gave an impetus to whinstone quarrying and very soon two companies proceeded to take advantage of the opportunity to participate in what was then a growing industry, that being sett making.

Basalt was quarried from the dykes mentioned from early days. Many of the outcrops along the course of the dykes seem to have been worked for road metal, building and paving stone. There is also evidence that setts were produced at some of the quarries. A fine example of its use can be seen in the ford in Great Eggleshope (980 297) though it is difficult to understand why two strips of basalt paving were inserted into a sandstone paved ford.

Slate quarrying (not to be confused with stone roofing slates) played a very minor part in the industry at a site on the Teesdale Inlier. However, more about these matters later.

It may already have occurred to the reader of this account that the coming of the railway to Middleton in 1868 was indeed providential. Employment had (apart from farming) depended for a century or more on lead mining which reached its peak round about 1870, after which it went into decline and, apart from a few small ventures, ceased altogether in 1902 when the London Lead Company gave up their leases. As will be seen later, without the railway, quarrying could not have developed in the way that it did. As the lead mines closed or reduced their workforce the quarries developed and very largely absorbed those leaving mining. As far as can be estimated, by 1900 there were employed at four quarries within two miles of Middleton more than 350 men and boys. And as road transport developed at a later date other quarries at a distance from the rail head increased production providing further employment.

A consultation of the early editions of the six inch and twenty five inch OS sheets for the area under review will prove to be a rewarding exercise for those wishing to be further informed. Names such as 'Old Quarry' or 'Quarry' will be seen with regularity. Not so common will be names such as 'Slate Edge' and 'Slate Quarry Moss' indicating places where slates have been quarried, or 'Millstone Hill' where millstones have been quarried and fashioned.

Very few of the quarries are in a dangerous condition, but access to the top of the face should be avoided where both the overburden and rock are often unstable. As far as visiting active quarries is concerned a courteous approach to the manager should be made, remembering that operations are taking place which could be dangerous to unaccompanied visitors. In all cases the Country Code should be adhered to in order to preserve good relations with the owners and farmers on whose land many of the inactive older quarries are situated.

A guide to the main quarries including those of historical or other interest

The order of listing is from the top of the dale. All grid references are in NY section unless otherwise stated.

Near Quarry, Harwood Common (Limestone) – 791 351

In the Scar Limestone and used until about 1930 by Durham County Council for the production of road making materials to be used locally.

Hill Top Quarry, Harwood (Limestone) – 825 337

In the Tyne Bottom Limestone. An exceptionally good dark blue rock which was used by Durham County Council for the supply of road making materials to be used locally.

Harthope Top Quarry (Ganister) – 863 342

Grid reference represents centre of area worked. The quarrying of ganister here commenced about 1920 and was spasmodic until the 1930s when General Refractories took over the lease and for some twenty-five years extracted large quantities of rock which were despatched to their works. Since they ceased work only small amounts have been quarried for building stone.

Church Bowers Quarry (Sandstone) – 873 324

Not worked since about 1925, but in its heyday produced a large quantity of exceptionally good durable building stone, flags and slates which were carted down the track to Forest and Ettersgill. The product of this quarry can still be identified in many of the buildings, though often covered by whitewash. However, Forest and Ebenezer Methodist Chapels are good examples of its use as is Bowlees Bridge which was the last building of any size to be supplied in 1922–23. In the construction of this bridge can also be seen a good example of Dunn House Quarry sandstone.

Malkin Quarry (Limestone) – 868 311

This quarry in the Great Limestone is also the site of the Teesdale Caves and is one of the places where hand-broken limestone was produced for local road surfacing. Lime in small quantities was also produced for local whitewashing, building and spreading on the land. It has been redundant since about 1937 and the kiln is now in a ruinous state. Adjacent are the remains of an ancient small kiln where use has been made of a cleft in the limestone face when it was constructed.

Carr Crags Quarry (Sandstone) – 918 316

A quarry in the Millstone Grit which was extensively used until the end of the nineteenth century for the production of a great variety of dressed stone-work including millstones, coping stone, gateposts, lintels, sills, steps, quoins, roof ridging, jambs and troughs of various shapes and sizes. The discovery of a peculiar shaped trough and the upper part of a rotary quern in Newbiggin, which corresponds to the type of coarse stone found at Carr Crags suggests that the quarry could be ancient. A number of millstones still remain scattered around the quarry.

Some of the millstones which can be seen at Carr Craggs Quarry. Several others can be seen including some only partly fashioned.

High Force Quarry crushing and screening plants photographed in 1931 with the quarry behind. The plant on the right was erected in 1911 and the other in 1930. Note on the right a solid tyred Peerless wagon under one of the chutes waiting to be loaded and on the left a cooling tower and large diesel oil storage tank. The nearest building housed the large engine, compressor and transmission gear.

The Quarrels Quarry (Limestone) – 861 305

At one time a Common Quarry in the Scar Limestone where the Commoners of the Township of Forest and Frith could exercise their right to quarry stone for their own use and use the kiln to produce lime. Later, it was used by Durham County Council for the production of road materials and became unused about 1920.

Pencil Mill Quarry (Slate) – 848 295

Site of the Pencil Mill where the outcropping Skiddaw Slate was both quarried and mined, ground down and moulded into slate pencils between 1850 and 1880. The remains of the mill can still be seen and the millstones, which are of German origin, are now lying outside Bowlees Visitor Centre.

Dufton Moss Quarry (Whinstone) – 872 292

Begun in 1931 by Durham and Yorkshire Whinstone Co Ltd, remaining active until 1941 during which period was produced both dry, tarred and bitumenized road materials. At the end of the war (1945) the plant and quarry were bought by George Hodsman and Sons (1928) Ltd, but remained idle until 1964 when the site was cleared.

High Force Quarry (Whinstone) – 879 290

Many of the quarries were begun where there was an outcrop of rock by the road side. High Force is a typical example, started in 1909 by two sett makers, Joe Allen and Tom Wardle. It was, however, soon taken over by a York man, George Hodsman (the founder of the company mentioned above) who was then in possession of other ventures lower down the dale which will be referred to later. A steam-driven crushing and screening plant was erected to produce 2½ in, 1½ in, ½ in, ¼ in, and fine. Setts were also produced in quantity.

Transport in the early days was by horse and cart to Middleton Station, supplemented later by a steam tractor which drew a large trailer. Motor transport was employed from about 1919 by which time production had increased. Then in 1930 there was erected plant and machinery capable of producing large quantities of the smaller sizes. Steam was dispensed with in favour of a Petter 240 hp diesel engine which later gave way to electric power. Later, in about 1960 the quarry fell into disuse in favour of the next one to be mentioned and the plant was dismantled.

Forcegarth Quarry (Whinstone) – 873 282

Begun in 1932 when the company was seeking to increase production still further, and upon realising that High Force Quarry was lacking in potential because of the fact that it was in the top part of the sill which would soon become covered by sedimentary rocks. Two large electrified crushing and screening plants were erected in a position from where the sill could be quarried from its base. Both were designed to produce large quantities of stone to be used as road material and concreting aggregates. In 1963 the company was taken over by Hargreaves Group Ltd, who replaced all the plant and machinery and included macadam and asphalt plants. The quarry was fully mechanised and now has a face reaching 180 feet in height.

Bowlees Quarry (Limestone) – 907 284

Begun in 1920 by Bowlees Quarry Company in the Scar Limestone. The product was first of all despatched to the iron and steel works of Teesside, but very soon hand-broken stone was produced for local road surfacing. The stone was quarried and delivered in lumps of up to about one hundredweight to the breakers who were paid two shillings (10p) per ton to break it

Forcegarth Quarry crushing and screening plant with the beginnings of the quarry behind photographed in 1933. The left plant was first to be erected to produce sizes from ¾in down to fine, followed by the other which was designed to produce larger sizes beginning at 3in including the smaller grades. This was nearing completion when the photograph was taken.

Forcegarth Quarry with the new plant and machinery installed in 1964. Since that time the quarry has been extensively developed with additional plant and machinery.

down to 2 in, plus sixpence (3p) per ton for filling it into narrow gauge tubs and transporting it to the hopper some distance away. In 1935 a combined crushing, screening and macadam plant was erected and a variety of road making materials was distributed over a wide area until 1946 when the quarry was worked out. The plant, however, was still operated by taking its supplies from Stable Green Quarry until 1968 when both places ceased work. That the quarry began a few yards upstream from the present picnic site toilet block, and that the plant stood a few feet towards the hillside from the same building may be difficult for the visitor to imagine.

Stable Green Quarry (Limestone) – 918 282
Development in the Great Limestone was begun here in 1946 where there was a small outcrop of about fifteen feet in height, which meant that the quarry had to be sunk as quickly as

possible to a lower level in order that a crushing and screening plant could be erected. This did in fact take place in 1953 and, as stated above, operations ceased in 1968 and the plant was dismantled.

paved with Teesdale setts. It was soon discovered, however, that the sill was not at its best and that the life of the quarry was in any case limited, so in order to be assured of quality stone with potential for development it was decided to extend the

Skears Quarry Lime Kilns. The ones on the right built in 1941 had partly collapsed by the time the photograph was taken in 1968.

Skears Quarry (Limestone) – 948 273

The use of this quarry in the Great Limestone and its kiln(s) can be traced from the beginning of the nineteenth century. However, incorporated on 12th day of January, 1937 was a private limited company which took over all the assets of Bowlees Quarry Company, and towards the end of the same year acquired Skears which was then standing idle. The kilns were repaired and progressively put into operation to produce lime which was supplied to occupiers of agricultural land under a scheme whereby the Ministry of Agriculture and Fisheries subsidised the user by 50 percent on the delivered price (the subsidy was increased to 75 percent for a period towards the end of the war). A further large kiln was built in 1941 making a battery of four giving a total production of 600–700 tons per month. After twenty-two years production ceased because high grade lime was priced out of the market which became flooded with cheap waste products.

Low Quarry – 947 245,
Park End – 924 256,
Crossthwaite – 926 254 (all Whinstone)

Low Quarry was commenced immediately after the railway came to Middleton by two Darlington Victorian entrepreneurs called J R Ord and H Maddison, who became the founders of the well known quarrying company Ord and Maddison Limited. In addition to large quantities of road materials, thousands of tons of setts were produced to satisfy the rising demand made by towns and cities, particularly in the West Riding of Yorkshire, where miles upon miles of streets were

standard gauge railway, which was already in Low Quarry, to Park End where a new quarry was started. This was very soon abandoned in favour of Crossthwaite which proved to be stone of excellent quality as can be seen today. Low Quarry was still worked until about 1930 after which quarrying was confined to Crossthwaite, though it should be said that there was maintained a whinstone washing plant and at one time a macadam plant which was supplied from Crossthwaite.

However, after more than a century during which at one time the labour force exceeded 200 quarrying ceased at the beginning of 1971, and more recently the plant and machinery has been dismantled. A fine view of all three sites can be obtained from Middleside road on the opposite side of the valley.

Selset Quarry (Limestone) – 916 221

Begun in the Scar Limestone in 1958 to supply filter material for the adjacent Selset Dam. Later the limestone was ground down fine and supplied in that form to the iron and steel industry on Teesside, but unfortunately the silica content was unusually high which proved to be a disadvantage. After being disused for some years the quarry was successfully operated by Selset Aggregates Ltd. until January 1995.

Lunedale Quarry (Limestone and Whinstone) – 954 239
Greengates Quarry (Basalt) – 935 235

Lunedale Quarry was started very soon after the railway came to Middleton by a company headed by a man named Urwin, who was possessed of sufficient enterprise to drive a tunnel

Low Quarry with the first crushing and screening plant to be erected *c.* 1880, steam-driven and called 'Jumbo'. The quarry was equipped with standard gauge railways which were connected to the adjacent Middleton-in-Teesdale station sidings.

Sett makers huts in Low Quarry with piles of blocks and setts scattered about the quarry floor, *c.* 1875.

through the hill a short distance below Laithkirk Church to work both limestone and whinstone on the left bank of the river Lune. A 2ft 6in gauge railway was laid from the quarry to a railway siding at 955 244 along which trucks were drawn by a Black Hawthorn steam loco named Lottie.

Apart from the production of roadstone, setts were produced from the whinstone and there was also an attempt to produce limestone kerbs and paving stone by sawing which was unsuccessful. Unfortunately the venture soon ran into financial difficulties and the whole of the plant and machinery was offered for sale by auction under distress for rent, at the above quarry, on Monday, May 18th, 1885.

It was then that the concern was taken over by George Hodsman (mentioned earlier in connection with High Force Quarry) who, it seems, purchased the whole of the equipment and proceeded to operate the quarry, but more importantly, opened out Greengates Quarry in the basalt dyke (part of the Lunedale fault), this being connected by an incline to the same

A group of sett makers in Low Quarry *c.* 1890. Note the blocks of whinstone in front of the group which had been carefully prepared for making into setts of various sizes.

The first crushing and screening plant, which was steam driven to be erected at Crossthwaite Quarry *c.* 1910. The three steam locomotives seen were engaged on the extensive lines serving both Low and Crossthwaite Quarries and the line connecting the quarries which were about a mile apart.

siding. Lunedale Quarry soon fell into disuse, but Greengates worked until 1917 when the Blondin, which was used to raise the stone from the then sunken quarry, was blown down in a gale. Setts, roadstone and tarred macadam were produced. There was some difficulty in operating locos on the gradient which was quite steep. However, in 1910 Bagnalls of Stafford designed a loco (Zuriel) with an inclined boiler which overcame the difficulty.

Banklands Quarry (Limestone) – 972 230
Begun in the Great Limestone by Cargo Fleet Iron Company in 1891 in order to supplement supplies needed for their iron works at Middlesbrough. After years of intensive working the quarry was rendered uneconomic because of the increase in overburden and ceased production at the end of March 1911.

Bail Hill and Black Rigg Quarries (Sandstone) – 966 224
Grid reference gives the centre of the quarrying area which has, over a very long period of time, supplied thousands of tons of good quality building stone and slates used mainly on that side of the valley, but also in the village of Middleton. None of the quarries are active at present.

progressively equipped the quarry with modern machinery capable of producing a great variety of sawn and dressed stone which has been used in both building and restoration work. The quarry is now being operated by Natural Stone Products Ltd. who have installed still more modern automatic equipment capable of producing a greater variety of stone products. There

Zuriel. the loco built in 1910 to work the 2ft 6in gauge incline of 1 in 20 from Louton Siding to Greengates Quarry. Dry weight 9tons 5cwt with special sand boxes and restricted to a height of 6ft in order to be able to go through the tunnel into the lower part of the quarry.

Windy Hill Quarry (Sandstone) – NZ 022 216
A small quarry begun in the latter part of the 1920s to supply building stone for houses being built at Folly Top. After many years of disuse it is now being worked for building stone, slates and sawn products by Windy Hill Quarry and Construction Company.

Shipley Quarry (Sandstone) – NZ 018 208
Grid reference gives the site of the present quarry at the south-east end of an outcrop which extends for almost half a mile where building stone and slates are known to have been quarried and mined for almost two hundred years. The quarry for the last thirty-seven years has been owned by Shipley Quarries who produce building stone, slates and a variety of sawn products mainly for the building industry.

Stainton Quarry (Sandstone) – NZ 073 188
An ancient quarry whose early owners may be difficult to trace and where the rock has been identified as a quartzite sandstone. It is said to have been in use for almost 1,000 years and that from it was supplied the stone for the round tower of Barnard Castle. It has made a valuable contribution to much of the building in the town itself in times past. In 1929 it was being worked by Hartley's but work seems to have been suspended during the war after which it was operated by a local company later taken over by Raisby Quarries. Successive owners have

is a showroom and an attractive sales brochure which lists the many products available, buildings new and restored and something of its history.

Cat Castle Quarry (Sandstone) – NZ 013 164
It is said that this quarry was first worked when the railway from Barnard Castle to Tebay was constructed and that the massive sandstone was used in connection with bridges and other works connected with both this and the Middleton-in-Teesdale branch line. However, the quarry was further developed in the year 1896 by a contractor named Scott who used the product in connection with local reservoir construction and other contracts in which he was engaged further afield. After a long period of disuse the quarry was again reopened and is now being operated by the Dunhouse Quarry Company Ltd who have installed modern plant and machinery to produce cut and dressed stone for a variety of purposes.

Hulands Quarry (Limestone) – NZ 016 138
This quarry in the Great Limestone was begun by Ord and Maddison after the Barnard Castle to Tebay railway line was completed but it closed in about 1897. The next owner was the North Eastern Railway Company who reopened it in 1912 for the production of railway ballast and it worked until about 1938. An attempt to restart the quarry in 1948 was

unsuccessful. However, it is now in the hands of Bardon Group PLC. who have installed plant and machinery capable of turning out large quantities of road and building materials.

Kilmond Wood Quarry (Limestone) – NZ 023 135

Begun in the Great Limestone in the early 1930s by R. T. Dent, of Barnard Castle, who was then in business as a haulage contractor and was developed into a viable business with a modem crushing and screening plant. The business was taken over in 1947 by George Hodsman and Sons (1928) Ltd. who added a macadam plant. Along with the other quarries owned by Hodsman's this also passed into the hands of the Hargreaves Group in 1963 who eventually dismantled the plant. Since then little work has been done until 1990 when plant and machinery were installed to produce large quantities of road and building materials.

Dun House Quarry (Sandstone) – NZ 114 194

A very old and exceptionally well equipped quarry which has produced in the past large quantities of excellent building stone which has been used in many of the local towns and villages. Bowes Museum, built in the early 1870s is probably the finest example of its early use. Dunhouse Quarry Co., Stone Masons and Manufacturers of Masonry Products was founded in 1930 by Albert Henry Allinson, and is still a family business now trading under the name of Dunhouse Quarry Co. Ltd. Because of its modem equipment, saws, lathes, and automatic polishing machines, etc, plus a skilled labour force the quarry is capable of producing up to 100 cubic metres of dimensioned stone products per week and gives a nationwide delivery service. In addition, a substantial amount of the products is exported. Sales literature is available which tells something of its products, its equipment and its capabilities.

All photographs were the property of the late H. L. Beadle.

Glossary

Burnt Lime: Limestone (calcium carbonate) when burnt in a kiln with the required amount of coke releases carbon dioxide leaving lime (calcium oxide).

Freestone: Rock which can be cut or dressed in any direction.

Ganister: Sandstone with a high silica content and free from certain impurities.

Inlier: An area where the rocks of an earlier age protrude through or above younger rocks. The reason for this can be erosion or faulting.

Blocks: The sett makers first operation which was known as 'Blocking Out' began at the quarry face where he selected rock of the best quality and reduced it into manageable sizes, loaded it on to a flat bottomed bogie and transported it to the hut.

Setts: Basalt and whinstone setts were made in a number of sizes ranging from 3in x 3in x 3in to 7in x 4in x 6in. The latter being the most popular size for paving streets. The sett maker when fully trained could make any size without resorting to any measuring device.

Water-Bound: Before the use of tarred macadam a road surface was laid with broken stone which was then rolled, covered with soil and watered in by a water cart. This was in fact a water tank on two wheels with a spray pipe along the rear, drawn by a horse. After watering the surface was rolled off.

Special Minerals of the Northern Pennines

Brian Young

According to a common, if rather irreverent, seventeenth century adage 'A Scot, a rat and a Newcastle Grindstone, you may find all the World over' (Gray 1649). Together with the much better known 'Coals to Newcastle' these expressions serve to highlight the obvious fame and importance of some of the region's mineral products.

At least as long-established as the mining of coal was the mining of lead in the Pennine dales and moors. From an early date beautiful specimens of the various minerals found in the lead veins have been prized by collectors and mineralogists. Probably best known of these is fluorite – fluorspar or simply 'spar' of the Pennine miner. The Northern Pennine mines have yielded some of the finest examples of this mineral known. There is probably no worthwhile mineralogical collection in any of the world's museums which does not contain at least a representative suite of these beautiful specimens. Northern Pennine fluorite may thus have joined the Scot, the rat and the grindstone!

Fluorite is a common mineral and its fame here arises from its form and beauty. Less well known, even to some mineralogists, are several minerals, some of which are almost unique to the region. A visit to any of the world's major mineralogical collections will almost certainly reveal, in addition to fine Pennine fluorites, examples of some much rarer species which originated here in our region. Although arguably less spectacular – they lack the brilliant colour of much fluorite – these possess a beauty and fascination of their own.

Before looking at these a little more closely it is worth recalling that a mineral is usually defined as 'a naturally occurring homogeneous solid with a definite (but generally not fixed) chemical composition and with a highly ordered atomic arrangement. It is usually formed by inorganic processes'. Individual minerals are referred to as species each of which is defined on the basis of 'type' specimens. The locality from which the 'type' specimen was obtained is the 'type locality'. The Northern Pennine Orefield has the distinction of including the type localities for at least three species; barytocalcite, alstonite and brianyoungite. In addition there are grounds for believing that the original location for witherite may lie within our region.

It has long been known that the individual minerals which comprise the very many veins and related deposits of the Northern Pennine Orefield occur in a well-defined zonal pattern (Dunham 1990). This is particularly well displayed by the sparry or 'gangue' minerals, i.e. the non-metalliferous minerals which accompany the metalliferous or 'ore' minerals. At its simplest level this pattern consists of an inner zone, centred around Weardale and the heads of the Allendales, the South Tyne and Teesdale, in which the deposits typically carry abundant fluorite. Outside of this 'fluorite zone' the gangue minerals of the deposits, some of which extend into the Durham Coalfield, are dominated by barium spars. The fluorite and barium zones are almost always strongly defined: only in a handful of places do fluorite and barium minerals occur together in the same deposit. Striking lateral zonation of other constituent minerals also occurs but this does not concern us here. This zonal pattern is interpreted as the result of deposition of minerals by crystallisation from hot solutions as they moved outwards towards the edges of the orefield from 'hot-spots' near the centre of the field. Such zonal distribution of minerals is common within other world ore fields though that seen in the Northern Pennines is one of the most striking and longest studied. Indeed the wealth of research here has greatly influenced scientific thinking on similar ore fields elsewhere.

For the first three of our mineral rarities we will be concerned with the barium carbonate minerals witherite, barytocalcite and alstonite.

In the outer zone of the orefield numerous deposits contain abundant baryte ($BaSO_4$). Over 1.5 million tonnes of this mineral (known commercially as barytes) are known to have been mined and a small output continues today from one or two mines. Apart from the finding, from time to time, of some magnificently crystallised specimens of this mineral the presence of baryte here is unremarkable: it is one of the world's commoner minerals.

The Northern Pennine Orefield is however remarkable, indeed unique in the world, for the abundance locally of witherite ($BaCO_3$) (Dunham 1990). Witherite is a comparatively easy mineral to distinguish in the field despite it commonly taking a variety of forms. Its most obvious feature is its density (4.3). In our region it is most usually found as compact masses commonly with an internal columnar or radiating crystalline structure and often with a rounded nodular outer surface. It is most often a dull pale yellowish or yellowish-white colour and a faintly greasy lustre is distinctive. When found in old dumps it often has a chalky weathered crust of baryte. Its hardness is 3.5. Crystallising in the orthorhombic system its crystals are usually rather complex hexagonal pyramids or prisms or combinations of these (Figure 1). Famous specimens consisting of beautiful hexagonal pyramids were found at Fallowfield Mine, near Hexham many years ago and striking white hexagonal prisms were collected from Nentsberry Mine, near Nenthead. Nodular masses and lustrous creamy white complex crystals were common at Settlingstones Mine, near Haydon Bridge.

Witherite was first recognised as a new mineral in 1783 by Dr William Withering, a medical doctor better known for introducing digitalis in medicine. The mineral, which was eventually to bear his name, was referred to by him as *Terra Ponderosa Aerata* as coming from a lead mine on Alston Moor, though the precise location was not given (Withering 1783). It was not until 1789 that the mineral received its present name when described as 'witherit' by Hoffman (1789, p 379). Doubt was cast on the provenance of Withering's specimens by Watt (1790) who suggested that Anglezarke in Lancashire, where the mineral was also known to be common, may have been the

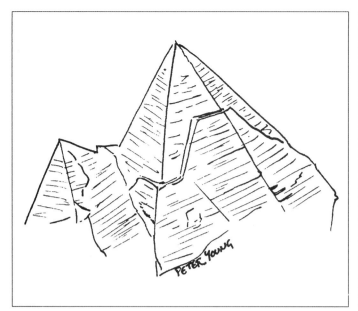

Fig. 1 Witherite pseudohexagonal pyramidal crystals from the Fallowfield mine near Hexham. The longest crystal is about 25mm long.

source of Withering's specimens. However, in a discussion of the type locality Selwyn-Turner (1963) regarded the claim of Anglezarke as less likely than Alston Moor. Notwithstanding Williamson and Williamsons' (1968) support for Anglezarke there is certainly a good case to be made for regarding witherite having its 'home' in the North Pennines. Whatever the truth is, and we shall almost certainly never know as it seems Withering's original specimens and documentation are long-since lost, witherite is certainly a common mineral in the North Pennines. Although found elsewhere in the world, e.g. in the USA, Austria, Germany, France, Russia and Japan the mineral seems to be found in greater abundance and concentration here in Northern England. The reasons for this are not understood.

Commercial mining of witherite, as a more easily usable raw material for the manufacture of barium chemicals than the more abundant baryte, began on Alston Moor last century. The world market was supplied from a number of mines, most notably Nentsberry, and Fallowfield, both formerly important lead mines in which the witherite had previously been an unsaleable accompaniment to the lead ore. In the early 1870s production of witherite began at Settlingstones Mine, near Hexham, which was to become the world's most famous, and for long periods sole, commercial source of this mineral. This mine had previously been a moderately successful lead mine. As the vein was followed south westwards beyond a crosscourse its content changed dramatically with the filling becoming almost entirely witherite with only minor amounts of other minerals. The mine rapidly changed to witherite production as it embarked upon a career which was to sustain it in its unique position for almost a century. During the present century a number of baryte and witherite-bearing veins were encountered during coal mining in the Durham Coalfield. Several of these were worked for witherite, the most famous being that of South Moor, near Annfield Plain. Here a wide vein, composed almost entirely of witherite was worked in conjunction with the colliery until 1958 (Anon 1940).

By the early 1960s it was clear that Settlingstones Mine, by then the sole remaining commercial source of witherite, was approaching exhaustion. Despite strenuous attempts alternative deposits of the mineral were not discovered and in 1968 the closure of Settlingstones brought world production of witherite to an effective end. At least 1 million tonnes of witherite are known to have been won from the Northern Pennine Orefield.

If the abundance of witherite in the Northern Pennines is difficult to understand then the common occurrence of two other barium carbonate minerals, is even more difficult to appreciate. These are the minerals barytocalcite and alstonite two of the three forms, or trimorphs, of barium calcium carbonate ($BaCa(CO_3)_2$). Although sharing the same chemical composition they are distinguished as separate species by their crystal symmetry: barytocalcite is monoclinic, alstonite is triclinic. The third trimorph, the very rare trigonal mineral paralstonite has not so far been found in Britain.

Barytocalcite seems to be a mineral which confuses many collectors, some of whom think of it simply as a variety of calcite, though many specimens labelled by collectors as barytocalcite are actually baryte. Until very recently one major British provincial museum displayed prominently a magnificent group of baryte crystals labelled as barytocalcite! There should be no such confusion. Firstly barytocalcite is a valid mineral species. Secondly it is not particularly difficult to recognise, especially when, as it commonly is, well crystallised. In its compact crystalline form barytocalcite usually resembles witherite. It has a density of 3.6, rather lower than witherite, but still noticeably heavy. It is commonly a pale creamish-yellow colour and, like witherite, frequently exhibits a rather greasy lustre. The hardness is 4.0. In the Northern Pennines it is commonly found well-crystallised with freely-grown crystals, commonly up to 10mm long, projecting into cavities. These are usually of distinctive appearance consisting of rather flattened prisms with sharp, oblique ends which at first sight give the appearance of the end of the crystal having been broken off (Figure 2). These crystals, which are often grouped together as fan-shaped aggregates, are commonly white or colourless: beautiful honey-coloured crystals have been found in a few places.

Barytocalcite was first recognised as a separate species by Brooke (1824). Although the source of his original specimens was not given it is generally supposed that they were obtained from Blagill Mine, near Alston. The mineral is extremely abundant here where, in places, it is the main constituent of the vein known as Fistas Rake which is in places up to 2.4 metres wide. The remaining dumps are today scheduled as an SSSI.

Fine specimens of barytocalcite from several hitherto unrecorded Northern Pennine locations are in the Russell Collection in the Natural History Museum, London. Clearly Sir Arthur Russell (1878-1964), undoubtedly Britain's finest collector and amateur mineralogist this century, had begun to recognise that this rare mineral may be more common in our region than had been supposed, though his findings were not then published. During the early 1980s the writer visited all of Russell's localities together with every site in the Northern Pennines from which witherite was recorded. X-ray

Fig 2. Barytocalcite
A group of monoclinic prismatic crystals from Clargill mine, Alston. The longest crystal is about 5mm long.

determinations confirmed all of Russell's localities and added many more giving a total of over twenty separate locations for barytocalcite throughout the region. At several of these the mineral was found as magnificently crystallised specimens and in some instances it was found to be the main gangue mineral in the deposit. Indeed at a few localities it appeared that it had been misidentified as witherite (Young 1985). Far from being a rare mineral in our region barytocalcite is quite common. It has since been found in the Mendips (Alabaster 1990) and Shropshire (Starkey et al 1994) though outside of Britain it remains a very rare mineral.

Late last century a few hundred tonnes of barytocalcite were mined from Blagill Mine and sold as an inferior grade of witherite for chemical manufacture. The discovery of significant deposits of true witherite at Nentsberry Mine effectively closed the market for the Blagill mineral (Dunham 1990).

Much rarer than barytocalcite, even in the area which bears its name, is the region's other barium carbonate, alstonite. The first specimens of this mineral which eventually came to be known by the name appear to have been found in the 1830s when Johnston (1835) described samples from Brownley Hill Mine, near Alston and Fallowfield Mine, near Hexham which, although having the chemical composition of barytocalcite exhibited a markedly different crystal form. They were referred to by Johnston as 'right rhombic barytocalcite'. Further investigation prompted Thomson (1837) to propose the name 'bromlite'' for this new mineral, the name being '…derived from its best known locality'. It was the German mineralogist Breithaupt who in 1841 coined the name 'alstonite'. This is the name which has since been generally adopted thus eliminating the early name based on the misspelling of the type locality.

Alstonite, like barytocalcite, when well-crystallised is comparatively distinctive. Its crystals are always complex pseudohexagonal twins, usually in the form of sharp bi-pyramids (Figure 3). Because of the complexity of this twinning the pyramid faces typically exhibit horizontal striations: in addition a vertical median, slightly re-entrant,

twin line is commonly seen on each face. The resultant crystals are perhaps best described as reminiscent of miniature church steeples, with the horizontal striations resembling the rows of tiles. Alstonite crystals are typically small: very large examples are up to 10mm long. Most commonly they are colourless or white but beautiful rose pink examples are known from both Fallowfield and Brownley Hill Mines. It is said that many of the pink specimens from Fallowfield faded to colourless or white on exposure to daylight. Like barytocalcite alstonite is a heavy mineral with a density of 3.7. It has a hardness of 4.5.

Beautiful specimens of alstonite from Brownley Hill, which exist in many mineralogical collections, appear to have been collected in the middle years of last century. Nall, writing in 1888, noted that the workings which yielded the mineral had then been inaccessible for some years and that even the smallest examples of the mineral were then attracting prices as high as £5 from collectors. In the past few years exploration of the extensive Brownley Hill workings has located alstonite in some abundance in workings on High Cross Vein. The specimens obtained are so closely similar to the original material that it is now believed that this was the source of the type specimens (Young et al 1990). A careful examination of the accessible portions of the Jug Vein workings revealed no barium mineralisation thus casting doubt on Walton's claim (personal communication in Spencer 1910) that this was the source of the original alstonite.

Magnificent specimens of alstonite, usually associated with striking examples of pyramidal white witherite crystals from

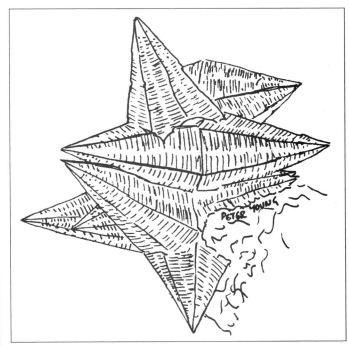

Fig 3. Alstonite
A group of sharp pseudohexagonal bipyramidal crystals from Fallowfield mine near Hexham. The largest crystal is about 3mm long.

Fallowfield Mine are to be seen in many collections. Like those from Brownley Hill these mostly date from last century. The remaining dumps at Fallowfield have, in recent years, yielded modest examples of the mineral. A brief period of excitement occurred amongst the mineral collecting fraternity in the late 1970s when an excavation made in one of the dumps to obtain material to fill one of the remaining open shafts, exposed an abundance of alstonite. Much to the local farmer's surprise and eventual irritation, collectors descended on his field from all over Britain and beyond. The excavation has now been covered and Fallowfield Mine dumps have now been protected as an SSSI for their alstonite content.

Elsewhere in the orefield alstonite was found in small amounts in the barytes workings of New Brancepeth Colliery in 1910 (Spencer 1910) and Sir Arthur Russell collected a number of fine specimens from Cox's Vein at Nentsberry Mine in 1931.

Although known from Illinois, USA, where it occurs in similar deposits to those of the Northern Pennines, and recently reported from South Wales (Alabaster 1990) alstonite remains, like barytocalcite, one of the world's rarer minerals, though not uncommon in the Northern Pennines.

The reasons for the common occurrence of both barytocalcite and alstonite in the Northern Pennines and their extreme scarcity elsewhere in the world, have not been satisfactorily explained. The types of deposit in which both minerals occur in our region are common elsewhere in the world. The essential constituent chemical elements, barium and calcium, are extremely common in such deposits and the rocks which host these deposits are also common. The processes which are believed to have formed the Northern Pennine deposits have their counterparts elsewhere. For whatever reason, however, the collective conditions required to form these unusual minerals in abundance do not seem to have been duplicated outside of our region.

The minerals we have considered so far are all primary minerals formed as part of the main mineralising process. Once exposed to weathering mineral deposits, like all rocks, are susceptible to alteration which may lead to the formation of a variety of secondary, or supergene, minerals.

The final mineral whose type locality is within the Northern Pennines is one of these supergene minerals. Described as recently as 1993, brianyoungite is a zinc carbonate sulphate hydrate. Coincidentally this mineral shares with alstonite, Brownley Hill Mine as its type locality. Like most new minerals this was discovered by accident. Samples of veinstone from Wellgill Cross Vein, which carried small crusts of the very rare blue copper zinc sulphate mineral ktenasite, were noticed to contain numerous minute white ball-like clusters of tiny crystals. Analyses of these by Alec Livingstone, at the Royal Museum of Scotland in Edinburgh, did not match any known mineral. More detailed examination confirmed that this indeed was a new mineral. In order to characterise this and to have it accepted by the world of mineralogy a very great deal of painstaking analysis of the 'white balls' were carried out, both at the museum in Edinburgh and at Manchester University. This work revealed the composition to be $Zn_3(CO_3,SO_4)(OH)_4$. All that was then required was a name. Much to my surprise, and slight amusement, I was asked if I would agree to it being called 'brianyoungite'. After approval by the International Mineralogical Association, a description of the Northern Pennines' latest 'special' mineral was published in 1993 (Livingstone and Champness 1993).

During the work to determine this new mineral small examples of it were found on old museum specimens from the mines at Vieille Montagne, Belgium home of one of the last companies to work the Brownley Hill Mine. Brianyoungite has also been found at Smallcleugh Mine, Nenthead and has recently been found in much bigger specimens at a number of localities in Germany (Schnorrer 1994; Witzke 1994). In all of these occurrences it is present in the oxidised, or weathered, zone of zinc-rich deposits.

These then are the minerals which the Northern Pennines has given to the world of mineralogy. The discovery of the most recent of these indicates that new, and potentially interesting, finds do come to light from time to time, even at very well-known sites. Is it possible that this remarkable orefield has further minerals awaiting discovery by observant and curious collectors?

Acknowledgements
I would like to thank Peter Young for preparing the illustrations. This article is published with the approval of the Director, British Geological Survey (NERC).

References
ALABASTER, C. 'Alstonite and barytocalcite from Llantrisant, South Wales and barytocalcite from Holwell, Mendip Hills, England'. *Journal of the Russell Society,* (1990), Vol. 3, 1–6.

ANON. *Witherite (natural barium carbonate) and its industrial uses.* (1940), Handbook issued jointly by Holmside & South Moor Collieries Ltd and The Owners of Settlingstones Mine Ltd, Newcastle upon Tyne.

BREITHAUPT, A. *Holoedrites syntheticus oder Alstonit, Br Vollstandiges Handbuch der mineralogie.* (Dresden/Leipzig, 1841).

BROOKE, H J. 'On baryto-calcite'. *Annals of Philosophy* (1824), Vol. 8, 114–6.

DUNHAM, K C. *Geology of the Northern Pennine Orefield, Vol. 1 Tyne to Stainmore.* (Memoir of the British Geological Survey, 1990). GRAY, W. *Chorographia.* (1649).

HOFFMAN, C A S. 'Mineralsystem des Herrn Inspektor Wernes mit dessen Erlaubnis herausgege ben von C A S Hoffman'. *Bergmannisches Journal Jahrg* (1789), Vol. 2, 311.

JOHNSON, J F W. 'On the dimorphism of barytocalcite'. *Philosophical Magazine* (1835), Vol. 6, 1–4.

LIVINGSTONE, A and CHAMPNESS, P E. 'Brianyoungite, a new mineral related to hydrozincite, from the north of England orefield'. *Mineralogical Magazine* (1993), Vol. 57, 665–70.

NALL, W. *A handbook to Alston.* (The Wordsworth Press, Carlisle, 1888).

SCHNORRER, G. 'Brianyoungite, ein neues basiches Zink-Carbonat. Teil 1: Sieben Fundstellen in West-deutschland'. *Lapis* (1994), Vol. 5, 24–7.

SELWYN-TURNER, J. 'The type locality of witherite'. *Mineralogical Magazine* (1963), Vol. 33, 431–2.

SPENCER, L J. 'On the occurrence of alstonite and ullmanite (a species new to Britain) in a barytes-witherite vein at New Brancepeth Colliery, near Durham'. *Mineralogical Magazine* (1910), Vol. 15, 302–11.

STARKEY, R E, HUBBARD, N and YOUNG, B. 'Barytocalcite and witherite from Rorrington Mine, Chirbury, Salop, England'. *Journal of the Russell Society* (1994), Vol. 5, 115–8.

THOMSON, T. 'On the right rhombic baryto-calcite with reference to Prof Johnston's paper in the Philosophical Magazine for May 1837'. *Philosophical Magazine* (1837), Vol. 11, 45–8.

WATT, J. 'Some account of a mine in which the aerated barytes is found'. *Memoirs of the Manchester Literary and Philosophical Society* (1790), Vol. 3, 598–609.

WILLIAMSON, I A and Williamson, P M. 'Withering and witherite'. *Pharmaceutical Journal* (August 10, 1968), 139.

WITHERING, W G. *Outline of mineralogy translated from the original of Sir Torbern Bergman.* (Birmingham, 1783).

WITZKE, T. 'Brianyoungite, ein neues basiches Zink- Carbonat. Teil II: Sechs Fundstellen in Ostdeutschland. Brianyoungite aus Sachsen und Thuringen'. *Lapis* (1994), Vol. 5, 28.

YOUNG, B. 'The distribution of barytocalcite and alstonite in the Northern Pennine Orefield'. *Proceedings of the Yorkshire Geological Society* (1985), Vol. 45, 199–206.

YOUNG, B. 'Alstonite in situ at Brownley Hill Mine, Nenthead, Cumbria'. *Mineralogical Magazine* (1990), Vol. 54, 515–6.

A Walk in the Upper Nent Valley

Brian Short

My father emerging from Haggs Level 1951

Photograph: property of author

Foreword

In writing this article, my aim was not to give a full account of the history of mining and associated operations in the Nent valley, only to state a few facts about each place of interest passed along the way. This I hope to have achieved to benefit the exploring walker who has a curiosity interest in his immediate surroundings.

My only request is that the inexperienced do not explore the shafts and levels, as sometimes they can be in a dangerous condition.

When I was young, this was my valley. Even today I still like to call it home.

I have several hobbies, not least of which are walking, industrial archaeology and photography, and these three can be combined and followed to a great extent in the upper Nent valley. This interesting walk covers a distance of approximately four miles, including detours and returns to the village of Nenthead from the head of the valley.

All map references refer to Ordnance Survey Outdoor Leisure Map 31.

Although concentrated around Nenthead, there are lead mining remains all along the valley so it was difficult to decide where to begin the walk. Because of the 'near miss' story associated with Hudgill Burn Mine the starting point was going to be Hudgill Burn bridge (753 460). The history of the mine illustrates the extremes of fortune often associated with so precarious a venture as lead mining and is well worth recording here even though the walk proper begins a little way up the valley. The London Lead Company (sometimes called the Quaker Company) held the lease for this mine in 1799, but their workings were without success and abandoned in 1808. The Flow Edge Company were operating in the area at the time, driving a level 1,500 ft long on the Hudgill Burn Vein System, discovering some flat mineralisation, but that venture too was abandoned in 1804 having cost £2,000. John and Jacob Walton took up the lease in 1812, continuing the Flow Edge Co. level but slightly to the south. In 1814 a good vein was discovered with large associated flats and in nine weeks of working, four miners won 120 tons of ore, and yearly profits averaged £30,000, a fortune in those days. The mine closed soon after 1870, having produced a total of 54,642 tons of lead concentrates. The ore had a higher than average silver content for the Nent mines, for example, recovery amounted to 13 oz of silver per ton of lead for the period 1854–70. Very little remains on the surface now, apart from a large spoil heap and the ruins of a mine shop, to give any indication of the prosperity this mine enjoyed.

Having got that story out of the way, my starting point is now what was, until recently, the Horse and Wagon public house on the A689 (758 458). This was built in the early seventeenth century as one of the residences of the Earl of Derwentwater, who owned the Alston Moor Estates, and the attached mineral rights, until 1715. At this time he was a leading figure in the Jacobite Rebellion and when the uprising was put down, his property and estates were confiscated by the Crown and later handed over to the Greenwich Hospital Trust. Religion had a very strong hold in the area and, indeed, there is a Methodist Chapel dated 1825, standing across the road from the inn, obviously sited there for the benefit of those with weaker wills in the hope that they might see the error of their ways, and mend them accordingly!

Behind the house, there are two or three sets of mine tubs, of varying antiquity, standing on a short tramway. These are typical of the tubs used in the mines passed on the walk, although many other different types were also used.

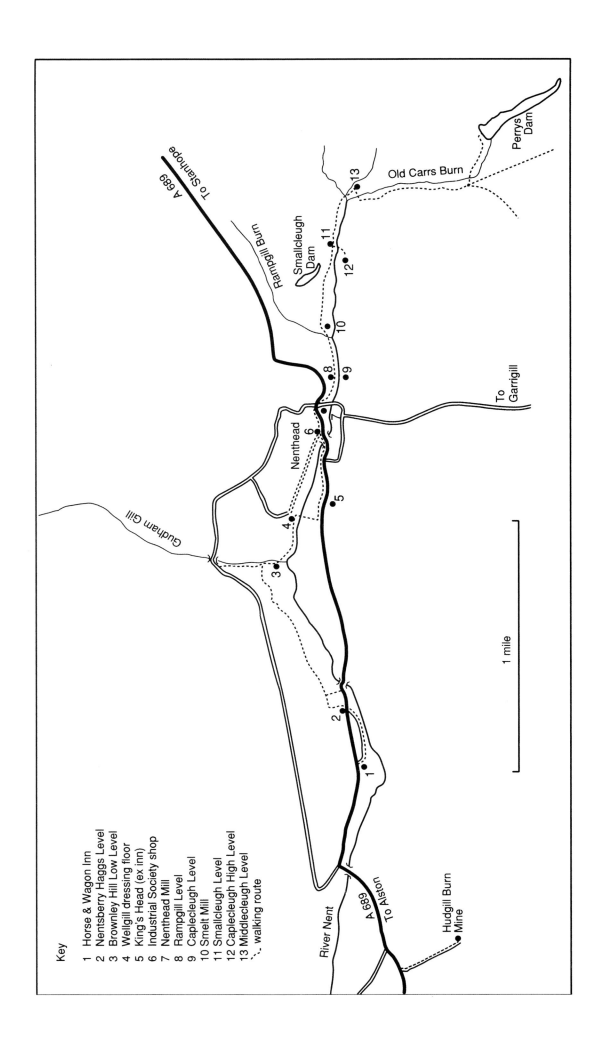

Key

1 Horse & Wagon Inn
2 Nentsberry Haggs Level
3 Brownley Hill Low Level
4 Wellgill dressing floor
5 King's Head (ex inn)
6 Industrial Society shop
7 Nenthead Mill
8 Rampgill Level
9 Caplecleugh Level
10 Smelt Mill
11 Smallcleugh Level
12 Caplecleugh High Level
13 Middlecleugh Level
-- walking route

A 689

To Stanhope

Rampgill Burn

Smallcleugh
Dam

Old Carrs Burn

Perrys
Dam

13

11

12

10

9

8

6

Nenthead

To
Garrigill

5

4

3

2

1

1 mile

Gudham Gill

River Nent

A 689
To Alston

Hudgill Burn
Mine

The track upstream from where the tubs are standing leads to the site of the Haggs washing plant which had the capacity to treat six tons of material per hour, brought out from the mine across the road. Zinc concentrates were produced here as well as lead, but problems were encountered in separating sphalerite from witherite, which has the same specific gravity, both minerals being combined in the same vein in the mine. The problem was eventually overcome by jigging out the lead and sending the rest by road to the Blaydon Alkali Co. near Newcastle, where it was chemically separated, the sphalerite being returned to Nenthead for treatment in the dressing plant. The buildings were demolished in 1949.

Close to the house, the round stone wall protects the top of the Nentsberry Shaft, sunk onto the John Smeaton engineered Nent Force Level, 340 ft below. A winding engine was situated above the shaft, and water from Haggs Level was directed down the shaft to turn a waterwheel which operated bellows, providing ventilation for the mine. Nent Force level changes elevation at this point, coming in at 890 ft AOD and carrying on to Nenthead at 1,050 ft AOD.

On the other side of the river are two portals, the left one being the original main horse level and the other being driven at a later date to ease disposal of waste material from the workings. This was the lower level of the Grassfield Mine, details of which will follow later. In later years the level served as a magazine for explosives used in Haggs Mine. It made the TV news in the 1970s when some mine explorers came upon cases of weeping dynamite. This was safely disposed of by the Army Bomb Disposal Squad.

Haggs Level itself is situated right on the roadside by the mineshop. Just inside the mine, the horse level rises at a sharper rate than is usual. This meant that the horse attained quite a speed virtually being pushed along by the full tubs coming out

of the mine and the trammer would often sit on one of the tubs or even run along behind the set. Because of this the mining company employed a man to warn approaching traffic when a horse and set of tubs were about to emerge from the mine. He sat by the portal, and upon hearing the tubs coming, he would sound a bell or wave a red flag. The system failed one day when the signal wasn't given to the bus which was passing on its way to Nenthead. In the resulting collision the tubs were overturned and the horse broke loose and bolted straight into the stables, and was found in its usual stall, calmly eating its hay as if nothing had happened. I can remember the school bus clattering over the rails which were still in position where they crossed the road. A large amount of water issues from the back wall inside the mine shop, coming from a blocked underground watercourse from the River Nent to the washing plant.

The date of commencement of mining here is unknown, but the Alston Mining Co. Ltd held the lease in 1821, the Nentsberry Mining Co. from 1894–1908, the Lugdale Chemical Co. from 1908–14, the Vieille Montagne Zinc Co. from 1914–49 and, finally, the Imperial Smelting Corporation Ltd by way of a subsidiary, the Anglo Austral Mines Ltd from 1949–53 when the workings were abandoned.

Incidentally, the British Steel Corporation took up the leases for the whole of Alston Moor in 1970, and they were followed in turn by Weardale Minerals Ltd, who, I believe, hold the leases today.

Deep inside the mine, the workings were also reached from the surface via the Wellhope Shaft, sunk between 1925 and 1927. The shaft is 416 ft deep, and was equipped with an electric winder and aerial ropeway, four miles long, linking the shaft to the Nenthead Dressing Mill. The ropeway was dogged with many problems during its short working life and the horse level was used for haulage, as before, the ropeway being dismantled

Horse and Wagon public house – formerly one of the Earl of Derwentwater's residences

Nentsberry Shaft from the site of the Haggs Mine washing plant

Haggs Mine and mineshop

for scrap in the 1940s. The main workings were on the Wellgill Cross Vein, Haggs Vein, High Raise Vein and a number of smaller veins around the Wellhope Shaft area. Production figures, though incomplete, are as follows:

Lead concentrates	1852–1938	40,617 tons
Zinc concentrates	1875–1938	15,091 tons
Witherite	1894–1912	1,600 tons

Standing by the level mouth and looking south a large spoil heap can be seen approximately 500 yds away. This is from the high, main level on the Grassfield Vein, opened in 1803, and producing 14,834 tons of lead concentrates. The original leaseholder, the Earl of Carlisle and Co. proposed an underground canal for haulage on the lower level, but this never came to fruition. The mine passed into the hands of John Carruthers and Co. from the 1850s until closure in 1885.

Available records state that silver recovery from this mine during the years 1854–64 was equivalent to 17.8 oz of silver per ton of lead.

Two hundred yards along the A689 is the Nentsberry Bridge, a fine sandstone block structure built in the nineteenth century to carry the then newly-routed road across the river. Being without any definite information on this point, I would imagine that the original route was the track on the other side of the river, suitable for the horse-drawn vehicles of the day, but becoming inadequate with the advent of the motorised vehicle, be it steam or petrol driven. One hundred yards upstream from the bridge, on the east bank, is a now fully silted up dam complete with the remains of a sluice gate. The captured water ran from here through a passage tunnelled out of the rock and across the field behind the mineshop to be used in the dressing plant as and when required.

At this point it should be noted that the path to the next place of interest, Brownley Hill (Bloomsberry) Low Level actually starts from Haggs Bank approximately 100 yds behind the mineshop, but a short cut is marked on the map, leaving the bridge at a right-angle to the road, by the side of the trees, although there is no access stile in the wall. If the short cut is taken, the path rises through the field for about 200 yds until a group of trees is reached on the right hand side. From here the walker is guided by yellow way-markers through a number of fields, keeping to the wall on the right. Eventually this wall is crossed a short distance before the path enters a small evergreen plantation. At this point it is possible to see, on the southern horizon, some of the dumps marking the shafts on the Greengill Vein, which was worked from the Grassfield Mine. Upstream, on the right bank, is what remains of the Brownley Hill spoil heap, most of it having already been carried downstream at times when the river was in spate. This was the usual practice in years gone by, being a convenient method of disposal of unwanted material, but fortunately it is no longer allowed. Opposite the spoil heap, on the left bank, is the first of five tailings dams, made up of the residue from the Nenthead Mill after it was converted to a flotation plant during the Second World War. In an effort to stabilize the sides of these dams, turves were laid in a grid pattern in the hope that the grass would spread and totally cover the material contained in them. This did eventually happen, but it took many years, because of chemicals present in the tailings.

There is a story which may or may not be true about a farmer who, at some time in the 1950s was foolhardy enough to venture across the dam on his tractor. Inevitably, the machine became bogged down on the still un-solidified tailings and despite the efforts of the local fire-brigade with winding equipment, the tractor disappeared below the surface, never to be seen again.

After re-emerging from the plantation the path skirts the dam and passes a house on the left. Although now being rebuilt, it was, until very recently, a ruin. This house, along with many others, would be home to lodging miners and washers. Now, sadly there are numerous examples of these ruins dotted around the village, serving as a reminder of those bygone times of hard-earned livings for many and prosperity for a few.

The path turns right upon reaching the track by the side of Gudhamgill, while directly ahead, over the beck, is the second of the tailings dams. Much smaller than the previous one, it has blended in well with the surrounding countryside, indeed its presence is betrayed only by the drainage pipe into the beck and by the material dug out by the burrowing rabbits.

A short detour to the left here will take the walker up to the high road which runs from Nenthead via Whitehall and Greenends to Nenthall down the valley on the A689. Brownley Hill High Level enters the hillside at the junction of the track with the road. This area is known locally as Buck's Bottom. Just along the road to Nenthead are the bases, on each side of the road, of support columns which carried the aerial ropeway to Wellhope Shaft. These bases are virtually all that remains of the ropeway, the scrap merchant having done his job well.

Back to where our track reaches Gudhamgill, one hundred yards down from there is the Brownley Hill Low Level (776 446).

When the mine was working, what is now a pile of rubble on the right was once a large mineshop with stables. A bridge crossed the River Nent to the spoil heap and the now replaced footbridge over Gudhamgill carried the wagonway up to Wellgill dressing floor two hundred yards upstream. There was a small building, possibly a candle-house next to the mine entrance, but this has gone the way of the mineshop, and become building stones for some other more modern structure. Two stone built pillars can be seen nearer to the river bank, these carried the tailings pipe from the flotation plant in the village to the first tailings dam and have nothing to do with mining operations at Brownley Hill Mine.

The mine itself was very extensive inside, having connections with the Scaleburn workings in Rampgill Mine and Scraithole Mine at Carrshield in the West Allen Valley. During its working life the mine had several owners, the first of which was said to be a certain Alderman Ridley, but the first actual preserved written record of the mine, in 1735, was at the general letting of the leases by the Commissioners of the Greenwich Hospital Trust. The lease lay unwanted for several years but was eventually taken up by Thomas Westgarth in 1748. He held it until 1751, after which time the London Lead Co. acquired the mine. In 1765 the lease passed to private individuals, W Armstrong and W Hutchingson, and then to the Brownley Hill Mining Co. in 1795. From 1816 the mine was worked by Jacob Walton on behalf of the Alston Moor Mining Co. before being returned, in 1874, to the Brownley Hill Mining Co. The Nenthead and Tynedale Lead and Zinc Co. worked the mine from 1890 until they sold out to the Vieille Montagne Zinc Co. in 1896. The mine then lay idle until 1936 when trials were made, by the Vieille Montagne Zinc Co. along the Gudhamgill Vein and some development took place in flats near the Wellgill Cross Vein. At the junction with the Wellgill Cross Vein and the main horse level is a down shaft with hoppers at the bottom. This was installed by the Vieille Montagne Zinc Co. enabling the material to be carried out to the day at Haggs Level and washed at that dressing floor, after the closure of the Wellgill dressing floor. The trials only lasted six months and proved to be the last time the mine was worked. It also proved to be the last mining done around Nenthead village.

Brownley Hill

Around 1817, a considerable amount of zinc was raised and smelted at the Langley Mills. Initially the selling price was £70 per ton, but this suddenly fell to £40 per ton and the operation was suspended. Better smelting methods were introduced and the zinc was taken to a new mill which was built near Milton station on the Newcastle to Carlisle railway in 1845.

The Scraithole connection was used for a different purpose one day when, owing to bad weather, a deceased person from the West Allen Valley was brought through the mine in a coffin, complete with mourners, for burial in Nenthead churchyard.

The principal minerals were lead and zinc with barite present in the north eastern extremities of the mine. Also present in small amounts were quartz, chalcedony and fluorite. Production figures are incomplete but those available amounted to:

| Lead concentrates | 1848–1886 | 18,328 tons |
| Zinc concentrates | 1872–1876 | 1,197 tons |

Silver content averaged between 5 and 7 oz per ton of lead

Crossing the footbridge and following the wagonway up the river, the remains of the last dam to be built, around 1960, are passed on the far bank. Owing to its small size, the dam increased in height too quickly, resulting, on more than one occasion, in a breach of the sides, allowing several thousand gallons of slurry to be released into the river Nent thus raising the wrath of the water authority.

Immediately after passing this point, the site of the Wellgill dressing floor is reached on the left. Not very much information is available about this dressing floor. The date of commencement of dressing operations is unknown, but the Alston Mining Co. were using the plant in 1817 to process their lead ore from Brownley Hill Mine. In 1880, the brothers John and Joseph Swan, who were to form the Nenthead and Tynedale Lead and Zinc Co, obtained the lease to process their zinc ore, which went on from here to be smelted at their mill on Tindale Fell. The area was landscaped around 1969 and now nothing remains except the manhole cover over the Wellgill Shaft on to the Nent Force Level.

Begun in 1776, the level was completed to this point, a total of 4.25 miles from the portal at Alston, in 1842, at a cost of £81,000. During its construction, only one vein of any importance, the Hudgill Cross Vein, was discovered, yielding a total of £4,200 of duty ore for the Commissioners of the Greenwich Hospital Trust. The level was carried on from the bottom of this shaft, which is approximately 200 ft deep to the Brewery Shaft in Rampgill Mine, some time between 1842 and 1856, bringing the total length to 4.94 miles, the first 3.4 miles of which was navigable by boat, this being the preferred method to the use of rails and wagons for material extraction.

The Nenthead and Tynedale Lead and Zinc Co. acquired the assets of the London Lead Co. on Alston Moor in 1882 for the sum of £30,562 7s 6d. Profits were made for some years, but falling prices caused the company to fold in 1896 when the Belgian Vieille Montagne Zinc Co. took up the leases for the mines and processing plants in the area. Wellgill dressing floor fell into disuse after 1896.

The tarmac-covered road which leaves the dressing plant area to climb the hill side behind passes the site of the Friends Meeting House, which was built by the London Lead Co. in 1722. Wallace (1890) states that a burial ground was attached to the Meeting House and there were seven interments therein.

The road carries on up the hillside and a right turn at the junction brings the traveller to the area known as Whitehall, before dropping back down into Nenthead to emerge in the centre of the village. An item of interest on that route is one of the faces of the clock which stood in the village. It has been built into the wall of one of the cottages passed on the roadside. Further along the road and just before turning right to go down to the village, there are some houses on the left. Two of these were converted from the Primitive Chapel, that particular building having the distinction of being the highest place of worship in the country. The building standing alone in the field opposite was once the main Vieille Montagne Zinc Co. magazine.

Back at Wellgill dressing plant and looking towards the village, two more tailings dams can be seen, one on either side of the river. The one on the left is the more recent of the two being used until around 1960, when Anglo and Austral Mines Ltd were using the flotation plant in the village.

The Church of St John can be seen further to the left on the hill side. As was the case with all the other public buildings in Nenthead, the land and the money to build the church and the vicarage was given by the London Lead Co. The church was built in 1845, in the incredibly short time of four months, this probably being the reason why it has been renovated four times since! Some of the interior fittings, which are mostly oak, came from an earlier church at Alston which was demolished in 1769. They are believed to date from the fourteenth century.

At this point on the walk, the River Nent is crossed for the first time. Crossing by way of the footbridge, the main road, the A689, is reached after ascending the bank leaving the river. Turn left here, and the second house to be passed on the right was formerly the Kings Head Inn, built around 1760, and one of four such places in Nenthead at one time.

A track leaves the road at this point and leads to Donks Hall Farm. It originally carried on to Fiddler Street, which in turn joined the Nenthead to Garrigill road, one of many built by the London Lead Co. in the early part of the nineteenth century. The interesting thing here is the name Fiddler Street. A fiddler, being an old name for a farthing, was the general fee to use a toll bridge or road and as the only other way from Nenthead to Garrigill was up the very steep bank from Overwater, too steep for horses and carts, it seems very likely that this was in fact a toll road in earlier times.

Just before reaching the next group of houses, Holmesfoot, are the remains, on the left side of the road, of the Greenwich Hospital duty ore bingsteads. This ore was a royalty paid by the mine operators as part of their lease agreement. The attached buildings have been pulled down recently.

Further on towards Nenthead, where the road from Overwater joins the main road from the right, is the end of the tailings dump. These tailings are the result of dressing operations on the Rampgill High Dressing Floor and the early years of the 'new'

mill under Vieille Montagne ownership. This dump, along with other dumps further up the valley, were the subject of an investigation by the Non-Ferrous Ores Committee of the Ministry of Supply during the last war. Sampling indicated reserves of 615,000 tons, containing 0.4 per cent lead and 3.5 per cent zinc. Processing this material in the flotation plant produced 19,941 tons of zinc concentrates and 1,385 tons of lead concentrates between 1943–46. The dump, even after this operation, completely dominated the village before being landscaped in recent years.

Just along the Overwater road and facing the dump is the school, built in 1896, replacing the former school, built by the London Lead Co. and opened in 1864 and later becoming the Village Hall.

One hundred yards further along the A689 crosses the river by way of the Nenthead bridge (779 438). The aerial ropeway crossed the road just beyond this point and the concrete base of the drive house can be seen on the right over the river on the side of the tailings dump.

On the left side of the road is a shop with house attached. This was formerly the Nenthead Industrial Cooperative Society and was built in 1871 at a cost of £280, the money being raised by issuing shares valued at £1 each. Dividends were paid from its beginning. Profits varied, falling as low as £4 for the year 1902.

The area opposite the shop was occupied by the magnetic separator house, a part of the Vieille Montagne Mill complex. The row of houses behind the shop, Hillersdon Terrace, was built by the London Lead Co. in 1825, to house their key workmen, smelters, agents and included a doctor's surgery.

Further along on the right is a red brick and steel structure, all that remains of the Vieille Montagne Mill, built for them by Krupps of Germany in 1908 replacing the old London Lead Co. Low Rampgill dressing floor, destroyed by fire in 1905. The new plant, which could treat 200 tons of ore in a 12 hour shift, using gravity separation, was one of the most modern and efficient in Europe. Power was provided by two 225 horsepower steam engines generating electricity. The lead and zinc concentrates produced were sent to the Company's smelter in Liege, Belgium.

It ran at full capacity until 1921, and then spasmodically until 1942 when the Ministry of Supply, along with the Vieille Montagne Zinc Co, modernized the mill with the installation of a flotation plant which could treat up to 1,000 tons of material per day. As stated before, between 1943–46 production amounted to 19,941 tons of zinc concentrates and 1,385 tons of lead concentrates. In 1949, when the Vieille Montagne leases were taken up by the Imperial Smelting Corporation Ltd, the mill was adapted to process fluorspar by flotation. This mineral came from Rotherhope Mine on Alston Moor and Heights and Cammock Eales Mines in Weardale. The mill worked at full capacity throughout the 1950s, closing in March 1960. It was sold to a Mr J Banks of Rampgill Mill Ltd for £7,000 in November 1961 and reconverted to treat lead and zinc, the latter again being sent to the Vieille Montagne smelter in Liege. This concern continued operations until 1963 when the plant and most of the buildings were dismantled and sold, mostly for scrap. Throughout its life as a flotation plant, the waste material was blended with water and pumped down the valley to the tailings dams.

In the mid 1800s, the old washing plant was fronted by a group of buildings, erected by the London Lead Co. in the interests of the local people, as well as their own workforce. These consisted of a school for 200 children, a clock tower built in 1818, a ready money shop and Market Hall built in 1825. Apart from these public amenities, a Post Office was built in the village in 1848 and a public water supply was laid on in 1850. When the 'new' school was built, at a cost of £2,000 in 1864 the old school was converted into a baths and public wash house with bandroom upstairs. This building remained until 1905, then its base became part of the aforementioned magnetic separator house in 1908.

Moving to the centre of the village, many more London Lead Co. buildings can be seen. These are the Methodist Chapel (1827), Reading Room and Library (1833). Behind the Reading Room is the former Agent's house and on the banks of Gillgill Burn is the former London Lead Co. offices. Overlooking the village from the hill behind the Chapel is the Village Hall. This was the new school mentioned earlier. The Miners Arms Inn was bought, and let, by the London Lead Co. in 1823, and apparently the rent was reduced several times as trade diminished, the miners preferring religion to beer drinking. The side road which curves away to the right between the Reading Room and the old offices was the original main road out of Nenthead, in use before the new road was laid as it is now. The field on the far side of Gillgill Burn is part of the Cherry Tree Estate, bought by the London Lead Co. from the Alston Brewery Co. in 1753 at a cost of £900. The large house on the estate was built for the main Agent and one end was extended to house the Company's main offices, which were transferred there from the previous site.

At this point the A689 is left to follow the road off to the right, to Overwater, but only for about 70 yds when a new car park is reached on the left. Personally, I find it somewhat difficult to understand the siting of this car park, as it covers the old Rampgill High Dressing Floor, and excavation would have revealed bousesteads, waterways and a washing floor, which together would have provided much interest to the modern-day explorer.

Through the car park and about 150 yds along the track is a group of buildings which were once the London Lead Co. woodyard and administration buildings. These were converted to hen-houses by a local farmer before the recent conversion to a visitor centre. In the corner, on the left is the entrance to Rampgill Mine (782 435). The fine mineshop and smithy were demolished some years ago and the stones taken away to be reused on domestic structures elsewhere in the village.

Rampgill Mine was commenced in 1735 by the Greenwich Hospital Commissioners after they had decided at the general lease-letting to keep the lease for themselves. Unfortunately their trials proved unsuccessful and in 1737 they sold the lease to a Colonel Liddell who held quite a large number of other leases in the area at that time. In the same year he built the smelt mill which will be described in detail later. Up to the end of 1738 Liddell's Company produced only 346 tons of ore worth £1,200 at a cost of over £6,333. His operations did not become any more successful and, in 1745, he sold all his leases along with the smelt mill, to the London Lead Co. Rampgill Mine was very extensive, working two main veins, Rampgill and Scaleburn, connections being made underground with Brownley Hill, Carr's and Smallcleugh as well as the Coalcleugh Mine in the West Allen Valley. The Nent Force Level proper terminates in the mine at the Brewery Shaft, although a smaller level carried on to the Low Whimsey

Looking over Nenthead Industrial Society Store to Hillersdon Terrace (white cottages) which was built by London Lead Company to house smelters and other important employees, to the old school (now the village hall).

Engine shaft further along the Rampgill Vein, 200 ft below the main workings. A petrol driven locomotive was introduced into the mine in 1902, but problems with exhaust fumes meant an early return to horse haulage, the locomotive being used outside instead.

Although incomplete, production figures for lead concentrates are given as:

| from Rampgill Vein | until 18?? | 120,000 tons |
| from Scaleburn Vein | 1848–1882 | 2,277 tons |

The latter had produced large amounts before 1848. Figures for zinc production are unavailable, but the Rampgill Vein was known to make a substantial contribution to the Nenthead total. The mine was closed in 1921.

On the opposite bank of the river is the portal to Caplecleugh Low Level. Although the horse level, and the main workings inside the mine, were the work of the London Lead Co, the Dowgang and Brigal Burn branch underground were developed by the Alston Moor Mining Co. up until 1871, when the Dowgang Mining Co. took over until 1885. W Dickenson worked the mine from 1886–90, followed by the Nenthead and Tynedale Lead and Zinc Co. until 1896 when the Vieille Montagne Zinc Co. became the owners. The other main veins worked in this mine were Black Ashgill, and Browngill, as well as the Middlecleugh Veins at the head of the valley. Underground passages, although on different levels made connection to the Whitesyke Level, near Garrigill in the Tyne Valley. There is a second portal serving the mine, about 25 yds behind the main entrance. This was driven at a later date to give easier access to the spoil heap, which was reprocessed during the war years and consequently no longer exists. Just behind the second portal is the Roundhill Dam which supplied water to both the Low and High Dressing Floors when they were in operation. The pipe across the river carried the mine water to the same destination. Beyond the dam is the tree-lined Dowgang Hush which worked, on the surface, the vein of the same name.

Caplecleugh Mine closed in 1921. Production figures are very obscure.

Following the track as it passes the walled wood yard, the remains of the Smelt Mill come into view. On the left, about 100 yds before reaching the gate is a site which was recently excavated. On it were the crushing stamps.

These were of the Cornish design and driven by a water wheel. It is possible to make out the position of the machinery from the excavations done. Stamps like these were used for two purposes. One was to crush the ore during dressing operations, the other was to crush grey slag from the ore hearth in the smelt mill, prior to re-smelting, as it contained up to 30 per cent recoverable lead. The stamps themselves are now in Beamish Museum awaiting restoration.

Just before passing through the gate to the smelt mill, there is a house on the left. Formerly occupied by the mill manager, this house has survived well and is now enjoying life as a holiday retreat. Rampgill Burn joins forces with the River Nent just downstream from this point.

The smelt mill (784 433) was built at a cost of £900, in 1736 by Colonel Liddell, in anticipation of good production figures from the various mines worked by his company at that time. He was confident that output from his mines would necessitate the installation of nine furnaces in the mill and indeed, there were four roasting hearths, four furnaces in the refining house and one furnace in the reducing house. As already stated, production never reached his intended level, and the mill, under his ownership, never worked at full capacity, even though he was also smelting ore sold to him by the

Remains of Vieille Montagne Zinc Co. washing plant (now a bus garage)

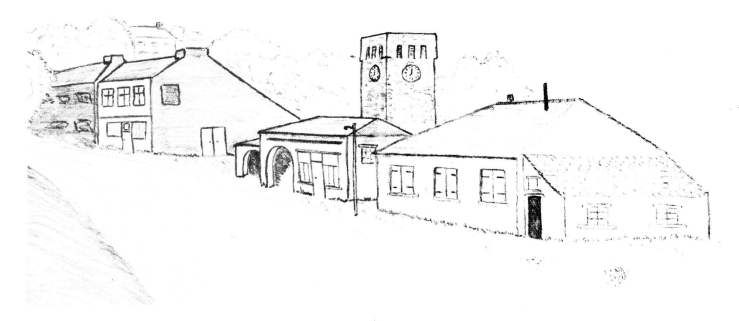

Part of Nenthead *circa* 1880.

Right to left: Wash house and baths, clock tower, Market Hall, ready money shop and warehouse.

Rampgill Mine and associated buildings before the recent conversion to a visitor centre

Commissioners of the Greenwich Hospital, obtained from their workings in Rampgill Mine. In 1745, the London Lead Co. obtained a transfer of Liddell's many leases, purchasing the smelt mill at the same time. They immediately redesigned the mill, installing instead two of the much more efficient reverberatory furnaces and one slag hearth. Smelting recommenced in August 1746. Many improvements were made over the years and a steady high output of high grade smelted lead was maintained by the London Lead Co, until their departure from the area in 1882. The mill continued in use under the ownership of the succeeding Nenthead and Tynedale Lead and Zinc Co. until 1896, and then by the Vieille Montagne Zinc Co. until closure in 1902. After 1902 the mill was dismantled internally and the buildings were used to house a steam boiler system which provided compressed air for the mines when the hydraulic compressors were inoperative.

Most of the buildings have either collapsed or been carried away piece by piece to be used elsewhere and the assay house

Site of crushing stamps, Nenthead

on the right is the outstanding feature today. This building contained a small furnace and other equipment to test the quality of the raw material, prior to smelting. In this way they were able to predict the resultant quality of the smelted ore, thus maintaining the high standard required to meet their specification on the open market. Opposite the assay house is what was most likely a lodging shop, but that assumption could be open to dispute. The smaller building nearer to the river was, prior to 1902, a stores depot, later becoming a magazine to store explosives for use in the mines until their closure around 1921. The pit between the assay house and the yellow brick wall beyond housed the water wheel which powered the furnace bellows. The wall itself supported the flue which carried the poisonous fumes away from the mill to the chimney on the fellside above. A large stone wall stands alone on the left side of the track behind the assay house. This is the site of the Stagg Condenser, built in 1846 and incorporated into the flue system to recover the lead oxide which was present in quite large quantities in the fumes. It consisted of three sets of bellows which pumped the fumes through chambers containing water and brushwood, the lead oxide separating from the fumes in the water.

By all accounts, this condenser was not as efficient as it was hoped to be and consequently other types were installed elsewhere. It was driven by a 40 ft diameter water wheel of the side-shot type. The rest of the flue was built as a double passage, enabling one side to be closed off whilst being cleaned, again to recover the lead oxide adhering to the inside surface, a very hazardous job as one can imagine, carried out, normally, by boys because of their size. At the southern end of the smelt mill site are a number of stone built bays which could be mistaken for bingsteads for lead ore storage. They were, in fact, built to store the coal used in the furnaces and later to fire

the steam engines. I can remember when the buildings were still standing in the early 1960s, but unfortunately a preservation order was not served to protect the site for future generations to see and the scant remains which are left today is a result of that oversight.

Leaving the smelt mill by the rough track, the traveller is faced with scenes of desolation and barren ground where nothing much grows, a situation brought about, jointly by the fall-out from the smelt mill, and the presence of lead and other minerals in the surrounding spoil heaps, which are mainly the leftovers, after processing on the Smallcleugh dressing floor further up the valley.

From this point onwards, several water races can be seen following the contours of the valley sides. The water being carried in the track-side race began its journey on the other side of the valley, picking up small streams on the way before crossing, and being supplemented by, the River Nent immediately below the compressor house, which is described later. This race fed the water wheels at the condenser and the smelt mill.

About 150 yds from the mill, between the track and the river is what remains of the 'shop' which served Carr's Mine. Built by the London Lead Co, it was still in use many years after their departure, when it housed Italian miners during the First World War. The shop door which, sadly, has now disappeared, bore several Italian names carved into the wood.

Carr's Mine is first mentioned, as far as is known, on the list of thirty-one mines offered for lease by the Commissioners of the Greenwich Hospital in 1735 soon after they acquired the mineral rights on Alston Moor. Bids were received from Hodgson, Hall, Whitfield and Haley, the last named becoming the eventual lease-holder. The mine was operated by the

London Lead Co. in the later 1800s and at some time in the intervening period by J Wilkinson and Co, and then by W Hall and Co. It appears on the 1773 Alston Moor Mines Plan shown as a short level heading towards Smallcleugh Cross Vein. The principal workings were on this vein and, to a smaller extent, the Hangingshaw Vein (East End). Production figures are not available for the mine.

On the far river-bank is the portal to Hodgson's Low Level. The early history of this mine is obscure and the only known plan, drawn up by the London Lead Co. some time after 1850, shows that the mine worked the Cowhill Vein and part of the Hangingshaw Vein. The latter was tested in 1822–24 by a Mr A Wilkinson who presumably held the lease at that time. His agent was Robert Hodgson who, in all probability, instigated the driving of the level, and, as was the practice then, had the level named after him.

Upstream from Hodgson's Low Level is the High Nent Force waterfall. The rock outcrop in this vicinity contained lead and indeed it was worked for this mineral, from surface by the waterfall, and underground from Carr's Level. There is a level on the Force Vein entering the bank side on the right, beside the waterfall, at the foot of the Smallcleugh spoil heap. On top of the spoil heap, at the end furthest away from the mine, is the North Powder House, built in the 1700s by the London Lead Co.

Back on the track, another rough track leaving from the left leads to the Firestone Level which worked from the Rampgill Vein at a higher level than Rampgill Mine itself.

Directly ahead and to the left is the Smallcleugh or Handsome Mea Dam (787 433). This dam was originally built to supply water to the Smallcleugh dressing floor opposite, and also the smelt mill, and when these two concerns ceased to be in operation, the water was piped to the hydraulic compressors at the bottom of the Brewery Shaft in Rampgill Mine, to provide compressed air for the drills and also to generate electricity for the Company's use. Nothing is left of the Smallcleugh dressing floor other than one or two concrete beds and some wooden flooring but, judging by the amount of waste material on the heaps it must have been busy for a long period of time. It was last used between 1905 and 1910, when the new plant was being built in the village.

Taking the track off to the right just above the dressing floor leads to the Smallcleugh Mine area. On the other side of the river are the remains of the bousesteads where the mined ore was tipped for preliminary sorting. The mine entrance and ruins of the mineshop are to the left where the river is arched over. Smallcleugh Mine is the most extensive in the area and is exceptionally well preserved underground. It worked the Smallcleugh Cross Vein as well as the Middlecleugh and Longcleugh Veins system at the head of the valley. One cavernous part of the underground workings has its own claim to fame. That is in 1901, twenty-eight members of the local Masonic movement held a dinner for themselves and their wives and other mine officials in the workings. To this day the sawdust is still on the floor, and if you are lucky you may find a piece of broken pottery among it, as I did one day. Old pictures show a blacksmith's shop standing over the river directly opposite the mine entrance.

Production figures are not available, because all the mines at the head of the valley were worked as one, and separate figures were not kept.

About 50 yds up the opposite fellside is a fine example of a London Lead Co. mineshop, although in recent years the stone roof has been taken away. This shop served Caplecleugh High Level, sometimes known as Hodgson's High Level, although my personal belief is that the latter exists elsewhere. Again, very little is known about this mine, but a grant to work Caplecleugh North Vein, which is very close by, was made to Mr A Wilkinson in 1754. The exact location of the workings in the mine is not known but, according to Wallace (1890) a dividend of £10,000 was paid one year so they must have been extensive. In 1780 the lease passed to Henry Errington and Co. and then to the London Lead Co. in 1799. The mine was later developed from the lower level and these upper workings lay idle until the coming of the Vieille Montagne Zinc Co, and with it new technology in 1896. In 1915 the horse level was extended to link up with the Bog Shaft, which went from surface down to the lower level, to coincide with the installation of the hydraulic compressors, similar to those in the Brewery Shaft in Rampgill Mine. The level was lined over its entire length with concrete and used as a spillway for the water from the compressors. There is another entrance to the mine, 100 yds away on the fellside, and this was fitted out with concrete steps as part of the same operation. There is a short drift in the shale beds in the fellside above the High Level but no information is available on it.

One hundred yards upstream from the Smallcleugh entrance, on the right bank, is the South Powder House, which was built by the Vieille Montagne Zinc Co. It was a steel structure, lined and shelved with wood. In my younger days it contained a wooden shovel but this artefact has gone the way of nearly everything else, probably residing somewhere miles away from here out of view of those interested.

In view directly ahead now at the junction of Carr's Burn and Longcleugh Burn is the Compressor House (789 427), again built by the Vieille Montagne Zinc Co. It contained two Pelton Wheel powered compressors, fed by water from Perry's Dam further ahead. The remains of the feed pipe can be seen coming down the Middlecleugh Level spoil heap, the scrap merchant having taken the rest away. The water from these compressors was also directed into Smallcleugh Dam.

The track which passes behind the Compressor House leads to Middlecleugh Level with its accompanying mine shop and spoil heap. This level was driven in the mid-eighteenth century into the upper portions of the Middlecleugh and Longcleugh Veins. Although some mining was done here, it is believed that the main purpose of the level was to assist with ventilation of the other workings below.

Back onto the main track, Carr's Burn is followed up the fellside past one or two obliterated drifts and numerous shaft heaps until the track splits into two. The right branch leads to Flinty Quarry, a sandstone quarry where most of the stone used for underground arching came from. Right at the next junction leads to Priorsdale, an estate first rented, and then bought, by the London Lead Co. in 1820, at a cost of £7,300. Five hundred and ten acres of timber were planted on the estate for use in the

Nenthead smelt mill in 1990

Caplecleugh High Level and mineshop

Compressor house and Middlecleugh spoil heap

mines and in fact, by 1840, the London Lead Co. had more than 650 acres planted for this purpose in the area. The track to the left, the one to be taken, leads past the stone-capped Bog Shaft to Perry's Dam (786 417), the end of the walk.

The combined volume of water in Perry's Dam and Smallcleugh Dam was reputed to be 20 million gallons, and even then at the end of a long dry summer, water availability was sometimes a problem, such was the demand at the washing plants and compressor sites in the valley below.

Perry's Dam is now largely silted up, but it remains as one of the many monuments to lead mining in the Nent Valley, some of which have been detailed in this walk.

The Nent valley has been a very important lead producing area from early beginnings when the mines were worked by small private concerns prior to 1730, through the period of concentrated activity, with its leaps and bounds in mining and smelting technology, in the hands of the London Lead Co, the Nenthead and Tynedale Lead and Zinc Co. and the Vieille Montagne Zinc Co. stretching from 1730 until 1920 and, to a lesser degree, up until 1963, at which time a combination of worked out mineral veins and cheaper importation prices sounded the death knell for a once thriving industry.

It may be estimated that the Nent mines have produced somewhere in the region of 600,000 tons of lead concentrates and 200,000 of zinc concentrates, a monumental figure considering that by far the largest part of it was won without the

aid of dynamite, pneumatic drills or electric lamps, only hammers, picks and candlelight.

Conclusion

In the Nent valley, Mother Nature will eventually win back what is rightfully hers in the battle against the ravages of man in his quest for that often elusive fortune. The mines are collapsing, spoil heaps are becoming rabbit warrens, buildings are being reduced to piles of rubble, helped on in some cases by man himself in his search for building stone for his house extension, and the tailings dams, once quicksand, then becoming dust bowls, are covering themselves with grass, blending in with the surrounding countryside. Soon, all that will remain will be books, photographs and memories. Speaking from experience, my advice is: 'Go there, take photographs and bring back memories, in respect of those men, and women, who worked so hard, sometimes paying with their lives, in an effort to make life more comfortable for their families'.

Notes

All drawings and photographs except the one beginning the article are by the author.

Drawings have been computer-processed to maintain their quality throughout the printing process.

The Duties of a Washing Agent
for the London Lead Company in Teesdale c. 1860

W. F. Heyes

The process of dressing and washing of lead ore in the mining area of the North Pennines has been extensively researched and described in historical, archaeological and practical terms. The conditions of employment and details of the labour employed on the washing floors, particularly with regard to the use of child and female labour have also been addressed by Raistrick (1965) and Hunt (1970). Little however has been documented concerning the management of the washing floors. It is true that the general principle of management in the London Lead Company is well understood and has been adequately described by both Raistrick and Hunt — i.e. the promotion of the most meritorious workers from the ranks to Overman (foreman), thence to Agent (manager), but details of duties and responsibilities are lacking. From the records of the largest concerns, such as the London Lead Company, some indication of the responsibilities and duties of Overmen and Agents is available but is necessarily vague; generally, a Washing Overman was responsible for the quality and output of dressed ore from his washing floor whereas the Washing Agent was responsible for the overall control and co-ordination of washing activities at several washing floors at mines within his district. Details of the day-to-day activities undertaken by these managers have received scant attention, probably because of a lack of documentary evidence. However, a recent chance discovery of a notebook used by a Jacob Readshaw in the Teesdale district in the period 1861 to 1866 has provided a unique insight into the working life and the duties of a Washing Agent employed by the London Lead Company in the mid-nineteenth century.

Jacob Readshaw was born at Hunstanworth, County Durham but by 1841 is recorded as living in Middleton-in-Teesdale with his wife Mary, also of Hunstanworth, and his children. He is described as a Mine Agent in 1841 and as a Washing Agent in 1851, residing at Masterman Place, the London Lead Company-owned housing provided for senior employees in Middleton-in-Teesdale. Jacob Readshaw was responsible for the management of the washing/dressing floors in the Teesdale district. The washing floors under his control ranged from Hardshins at Troutbeck, close to the watershed of the South Tyne and the Tees in Upper Teesdale, to Wiregill (Eggleshope) in the south and from Bollihope north of Middleton-in-Teesdale to Lunehead (Yorkshire) and Murton (Westmorland) on the western side of the Pennines. The black leather-bound notebook, measuring approximately 6 in x 4 in (150 mm x 100 mm) appears to have been carried by Jacob as he visited the various mines in his district as his notes were initially scribbled untidily in pencil, but subsequently over-written in a neat handscript in black ink. Not all notes have been over-written in ink and some loss of text is evident, but more than sufficient information remains to provide a clear, unambiguous picture of the many and varied tasks with which he, as Washing Agent, was directly involved. For ease of description the areas of

responsibility as evidenced by Jacob Readshaw's notes have been collated into groups and are discussed individually below.

Employment of Washerboys

Each year washerboys were employed to replace those boys who had graduated to underground workers. It was a general principle within the London Lead Company not to place boys underground until the age of 18 as they were not considered strong enough, or to have sufficient stature, to cope with the arduous conditions underground before attaining this age. Instead, between the ages of 12 and 17, boys were assigned to the washing floors where the tasks required less physical effort. Jacob Readshaw's notebook shows that the Washing Agent was responsible for selecting the washerboys from the applicants and for assigning the successful applicants to a washing floor. This was a particularly important responsibility because of the London Lead Company policy of succession planning — i.e. that washerboys would progress to miners and the most meritorious miners to Overmen, and ultimately to Agents. It was thus of paramount importance to select the most promising boys at the outset if the Company policy was to be successful. It is not recorded how the selection process took place but as Jacob Readshaw clearly had personal knowledge of each applicant, each being rated on a scale A to C in his notes, it is most likely that Jacob met, or interviewed, the applicants at some stage. Jacob would be unlikely to have a personal knowledge of boys living beyond the confines of Middleton and as applications were from all areas of the district geographically, including Westmorland, and totalled 60 to 70 annually during the period in question, this must have been an onerous task. It is possible that this job was undertaken as Jacob visited the different areas within his district during the year, particularly those outlying areas from where it would have been an arduous task for an 11 or 12 year old to walk to Middleton. No dates accompany the application lists so the length of time required to complete this task each year cannot be determined. A detailed analysis of the Washerboy employment applications may be found in a previous publication (Heyes, 1995).

Waste Bargains

Scattered throughout the notebook are various bargains agreed by Jacob Readshaw at the washing floors within his control. Although the agreement of bargains with ore-washers is known to have been superseded by the payment of wages by the mid-nineteenth century, in order to make the most prudent use of the mechanisation and manpower, some jobs were still considered to be more economical using the bargain system — in particular, the further washing of waste, slimes etc. to obtain additional galena for smelting. Bargains of this nature are recorded in the Blackett/Beaumont records (Hunt, 1970) and Jacob Readshaw's notebook confirms that the system was also in use by the London Lead Company.

Waste Bargain at Murton

Jacob Gray & Partners

agree to wash waste at Murton Fell, waste from the old dead heap and other waste from the old works and likewise from the beck.

The bargain to continue and end at 25 Dec 1862.

That they shall have 50/- per bing for well dressed ore. That they shall have the use of the tubs now standing on the place where the waste is. That they find their own sieves shovels colrakes and other small gear the same as other workmen in the Companies works.

That they shall have water from the bail up dam when not wanted for bouse washing, but they must not have water from the high tarn. They must be guided by the Companies washing foreman in the matter of water.

No advance money until the Companies Washing Agents are satisfied that it fairly earned.

Should they need the use of the grinder the Companies washers will serve them on the same terms the miners are served, but the said Gray & Part. will not be allowed to have the use of the grinder to themselves. No troughs or other gear to be supplied.

25 Jany 1862

Fig. 1 Replica of a Waste Bargain entered in Jacob Readshaw's notebook.

A bargain agreed by Jacob Readshaw with Jacob Gray at Murton, reproduced in Fig. 1, is recorded in full in the notebook. The duration of the bargain (11 months) is an interesting feature since the bargains with the underground workers are known to have been arranged on a 4-monthly basis by this date. Control of the Company interests is adequately demonstrated by the restriction on the use of water from the reservoirs and the overall authority vested in the washing foreman. The stipulation for the waste washers to provide their own tools corresponds with known practice.

Jacob Readshaw's notes give some information on the typical waste bargains agreed for the Teesdale mines and those for 1862 are listed in Table 1. Although no details of the conditions and restrictions inherent in the bargain are recorded it is not unreasonable to assume that these would be similar to those defined in the Jacob Gray agreement. Though somewhat sparse and incomplete, the available information again indicates an annual agreement of waste bargains.

Partnership	Mine	Designated Waste	Bargain (per bing)
Geo Lowes & Brother	Manor Gill	North Vein	45/-
Jacob Tallentyre	Lodge Sike	Old High Rake	45/-
Wm Thompson & Son	Lodge Sike	High Level	45/-
Jno Thompson	Lodge Sike	Grinder Cuttings	45/-
Peter Lee	Coldberry & Firestone Level	Dead Heaps & Gutters Dead Heaps	45/-
Geo Robinson	Skears Beck & Redgroves	Gutters & Dead Heaps	45/-
Jos Tallantyre	Flushimere	Old Floors	45/-
Thos Anderson	Redgroves	Low Gutters	45/-
Ben Lee & Partner	Redgroves	Low Beck above the grinder	45/-
Thos Lee (Holwick)	Manor Gill	Old Waste in Gutters	45/-

Table 1. Waste Bargains in the Teesdale area, 1862

Water Supplies

An ample and continuous supply of water was an obvious necessity for a washing floor and not surprisingly a large proportion of Jacob Readshaw's notes refer to his involvement in ensuring that this important requirement was not neglected. In order that sufficient stocks of water might be available during times of drought, it was common practice to build appropriately-sized reservoirs on the fells above the washing floors by damming a suitable area. Sketches of various dams are included in Jacob's notes together with estimates of materials required; dams in Bollihope, Howden Burn and at Coldberry are mentioned by name. The apparent emphasis on dam-building evident in the notebook may be a reflection of the extensive drought experienced in the Teesdale locality between the months of February and June 1861 and recorded in the Minute Books of the Court of Assistants (Raistrick 1935).

A dam in Bollihope was being considered in 1861 (Fig. 2):

'Bollihope Dam — The imbankment to be made 9 feet high above a stake marked A. The outside to slope 1 in 1. The inside to slope one in two and have a puddle [1] dike 3 feet thick on the upper face of it so as to make the imbankment watertite. No sods or fiberious substance to be in or near the puddle dike. — The area of the cross section is about 21 yards and will therefore take about 20 yds wide of earth to make it'

[1] Puddling, was the consolidation of the clay by continually treading the wetted mass to form a watertight seal.

The proposed site of the dam is not given. Indeed, there appears to be some doubt whether this particular dam was built for a note dated 1864 reads (Fig. 3):

'Bollihope dam may be got 200 yds long and more than 50 yds wide would be covered by water at 9 feet deep, would contain 30,000 cubic yds of water. — Might be extended to hold 40,000 cubic yds'

It is of course possible that both dams were constructed, the second dam representing the Company's contingency plans following the five-month drought of 1861. An estimate of the cost of building the 1864 dam is given:

	£ s d
Cutting and laying the earth for the imbankment	325 0 0
Pudling and attendance	45 0 0
Stoning the face of the dam	50 0 0
Caus wall extn	50 0 0
	470 0 0

Not only was Jacob involved in the design of the dams but he was also responsible for arranging the contracts or agreements for the building work. Thus on the 23rd March 1866 Jacob made the following agreement:

'Geo Hardy and Wm Tallantyre together or separate as may suit themselves agree to cut out a dam at Coldberry, make the imbankment, puddle the same to make it water tight, cover the outside with growing sods. The imbankment to slope 1 in 1 outside, 1 in 2 inside—at 7½d per cubic yard. The height 9 feet above a stake now fixed as a guide for the bottom of the dam'

Work began on the 30th March 1866. Other similar agreements are scattered throughout the notebook, such as that for Howden Burn Dam:

'Building a Dam in Howden Burn below Cornish Washings — Thos Watson, Henry Lee and Thos Lowes, contractors, to build the said dam 12 feet high above the sole of the dam frame on the west side of the frame and 8 feet high on the east side of the frame and to wall and pave the water way as directed for the sum of £20-0-0'

This agreement also confirms that, as might be expected, the Agent was concerned with the delivery of water to the washing floor, as well as with the provision of the reservoir.

Cornish Hush Mine

The period covered by the notebook, 1861 to 1866, was the time that Cornish Hush Mine was being developed and Jacob Readshaw's notes show the extent to which he was directly involved in this development. His involvement with the building of the dam and waterways has already been mentioned, but the construction of the dressing/washing floors and associated matters also received his individual attention. Thus in 1862 Jacob was planning the arrangements to build a wheelcase; on the 24th October he prepared from the measurements estimated costs for the stone work:

Total cut stone = 5890 feet		£.	s.	d.
@ 4d.	=	98	3	4
@ 3d.	=	73	2	6
@ 2½d.	=	61	7	1

2

Bolihope Dam

The imbankment to be made 9 feet high above a stake marked A

The out side to slope 1. in 1.

The inside to slope one in two. and have a puddle dike 3 feet thick on the upper face of it so as to make the imbankment water tite —

No Sods or fiberious substance to be in or near the puddle dike. —

Thos Archer & Part

Section A ~52
B ~40
C ~94
D ~3

1861

27) 18 2 7 /3
18 2 /21

A horizontal line *surface* *Cross Section of the imbankment ~21 yards* *Puddle dike*

Dam in Bolihope
The area of the cross section is about 21 yards and will therefore take about 20 yd wide of earth to make it. —

28

June 1864

Bolihope Dam
May be got 200 yds long and more than 50 yds wide would covered by water at 9 feet deep, would contain 30000 cubic yds of water, —
Might be extended to hold 40.000 cubic yd

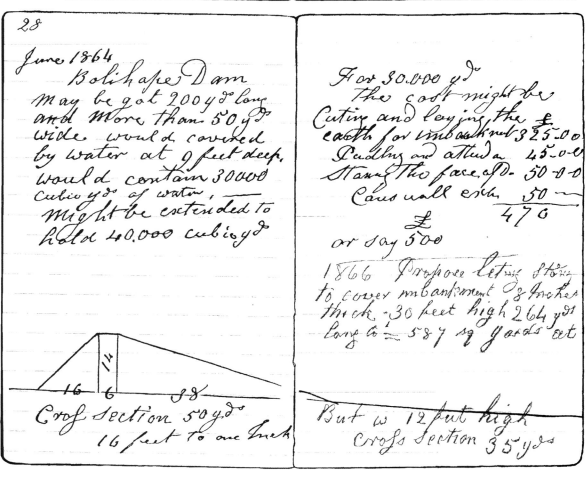

16   6   38
14

Cross section 50 yds
16 feet to one Inch

For 30.000 yd
The cost might be Cuting and laying the earth for imbankment £325-0-0
Pudling and attend 45-0-0
Staning The face &c - 50-0-0
Caus wall &c 50
£470
or say 500

1866 Propose letting Stone to cover imbankment 8 inches thick - 30 feet high 264 yds long to 587 sq yards at

But w 12 feet high Cross section 35 yds

No trace can be found of the Howden Burn Dam but the nearby construction on the Harwood Sike may be similar. The cross section and paved spillway can be seen.

Photo: Bryan Chambers

Total common stone = 2240 feet

@ 8s. 6d. per fathom =		10	8	3

Total cost of winning & leading

@ 4d.	=	108	11	7
@ 3d.	=	84	0	9
@ 2½d.	=	71	15	4

A subsequent entry in the notebook states that one Jos Collingwood was contracted to provide the cut stone at 3d. per foot.

By the 25th March 1863 Jacob had turned his attention to the bouseteams:

Winning stone for Bouseteams, Brest Wall, Pillars etc,
900 yds   @ 11s.   =   £45. 0s. 0d.

Many other supplies needed for Cornish Hush are listed in Jacob's notebook and it is probable that many of these, particularly the ironwork, were requisitioned by Jacob from the central stores and workshops located at headquarters at Middleton House, Middleton-in-Teesdale on returning from the mine:

Wanted for the grinder:

Flags	700 yds
Cundit troughs	400 ft
Presure pipes	24 fathoms
Smidum budles	3
Trunk boxes	3
Flanged troughs	3
Pit midles 16 feet long	10
Pit midles 112 feet long	4
Pit midles 96 feet long	6
Large troughs	260 feet
Regulating box	2

Beds for Cornish Mine—5 double bedsteads and bedding for 6 beds
Wanted at Cornish Hush, a cylinder for rough side—will the high rake one do?'

Summary

Although the above description of duties cannot be directly extrapolated to all Washing Agents employed by the London Lead Company, it is undoubtedly indicative of the wide ranging powers and management responsibilities/duties assigned to a Washing Agent and executed on behalf of the Company. Overall, the entries in the notebook confirm the expected level of responsibility held by a Washing Agent based on the well-documented management structure of the London Lead Company, that is, to ensure the efficient operation of the dressing floors within his district. The above extracts from Jacob Readshaw's notebook also clearly demonstrate the diversity of duties undertaken as a Washing Agent and two categories of responsibilities are evident. Many of the responsibilities were general in nature and required the Agent's attention on a regular basis — such tasks as the annual employment of washerboys or the agreement of waste bargains and contracts. Other tasks appear to be quite specific and probably represent the priority objective at that time. An example of this is Jacob's involvement in the setting-up of the Cornish Hush dressing floors and associated structures.

References:

Heyes W F. 'Applications for the Position of Washerboy with the London Lead Company in Teesdale, 1862–1866'. *The Teesdale Record Society Journal* Third Series (1995), Vol. 3, pp. 7–20

Hunt C J. *The Lead Miners of the Northern Pennines* (Manchester University Press, 1970).

Raistrick A. 'Some Pennine Weather Records of the 19th Century', *The Vasculum* (1935), Vol. 21, pp. 50–52

Raistrick A. *Two Centuries of Industrial Welfare* (Friends Historical Society, 1938).

Raistrick A. & Jennings B. *A History of Lead Mining in the Pennines* (Longmans, Green and Co., 1965).

One of a pair of reservoirs on the fell above Cornish Hush Mine which seem to be similar to the type described in the text as 'Bollihope Dam'. There is no proof that this is the actual dam. (*Ed.*)

Photograph: Peter Wilkinson

A view of the eastern end of the above reservoir giving some idea of the cross-section and construction of the dam.

Photograph: Bryan Chambers

The illustrations of notebook pages have been computer-processed to maintain their legibility through the printing process.

Mine Alone

J. R. Foster-Smith

My first introduction to mining in the North Pennines took place in 1937, when, on a cycling tour of the area I was given permission to visit Rotherhope Fell mine near Alston. This mine was then in full production and was a most impressive layout. The surface buildings were all substantial and modern, the gravity mill consisting of jigs and tables which produced a high grade lead ore concentrate. Underground one approached the workings through a long crosscut which I understood had been engineered by Smeaton. At that time all production was obtained from flats in the Tyne Bottom Limestone, which were entered through an incline sunk from the main level and were an amazing sight to my inexperienced eyes. The working faces were of some ten feet in height and full of strings of bright galena and many beautiful fluorite crystals. My only regret is that I did not collect more of them at that time since this place is now below water and the incline has in any case collapsed. This visit inspired me to hope for eventual employment in this fascinating orefield, but alas the war intervened and it was not until 1948, after military service and other jobs that I did manage to find such a position.

Rotherhope Fell Mine, 1990.

In 1948, I was appointed Mine Manager of Cowgreen Mine in Upper Teesdale, then operated by Anglo Austral Mines Ltd. a subsidiary of the Imperial Smelting Corporation, Avonmouth. It is about Cowgreen mine that I now write in order to give some idea of day-to-day happenings in those days

First a little background. Cowgreen mine was situated about eight miles north-west of Middleton-in-Teesdale and about one mile upstream of the well-known Cauldron Snout waterfalls. It lay in bare moorland country and the main site is about 1,500 feet above sea level. It was worked in the lowest beds of the Carboniferous rocks, centred upon the Melmerby Scar Limestone and the Whin Sill, which hereabouts is intruded into the limestone. Two main veins were worked, the most productive of which was the Winterhush Vein, but the other vein of importance was the Greenhush Vein, which branched to the north-east of the Winterhush Vein. The general layout of the mines area is shown on the accompanying map. The workings were entered through the Horse Level, which was driven north on the Winterhush Vein from near the main mine buildings. The lower workings were entered through the Wrentnall Shaft, which was also sunk from the same site. This shaft was sunk to levels at 106 ft and 191 ft depths, but was eventually deepened to 315 ft depth, as described later.

The mines here were originally worked for lead ore, but the galena content of the veins is very small, amounting to only about one percent of the total contained material. Most of the vein content was baryte and the mines of this area were chiefly worked for this mineral from an early date. Cowgreen was one of the largest producers of this mineral in Britain and the total recorded output up to 1954, when it closed, was some 300,000 tons of dressed material. The ore was dressed in a very simple gravity mill at the shaft head. This consisted of Hartz jigs, which were later supplemented by Wilfley tables.

It is not intended that this shall be a technical description of the mines, which have been fully described by K. C. Dunham in the *Geological Survey, Geology of the Northern Pennine Orefield, Vol 1. The Tyne to Stainmore*, HMSO, 1990.

At the time when I took on the management of the mine about 140 men were employed and weekly output averaged about 300 tons of dressed barytes, which was shipped by motor truck to Middleton-in-Teesdale station and from there to Orr's Zinc White Ltd. works at Widnes by train.

The veins varied in width from about three feet to as much as ten feet and were worked by a flat-back cut-and-fill system of stoping, since the vein walls were not on the whole very strong. The fill consisted mainly of mill tailings which were fed through hoppers from surface and trammed to the appropriate stope. Where this was not possible fill was obtained by chambering into the vein walls underground. The miners at Cowgreen were all local men and many of them were also part time farmers as was customary in Teesdale at that time.

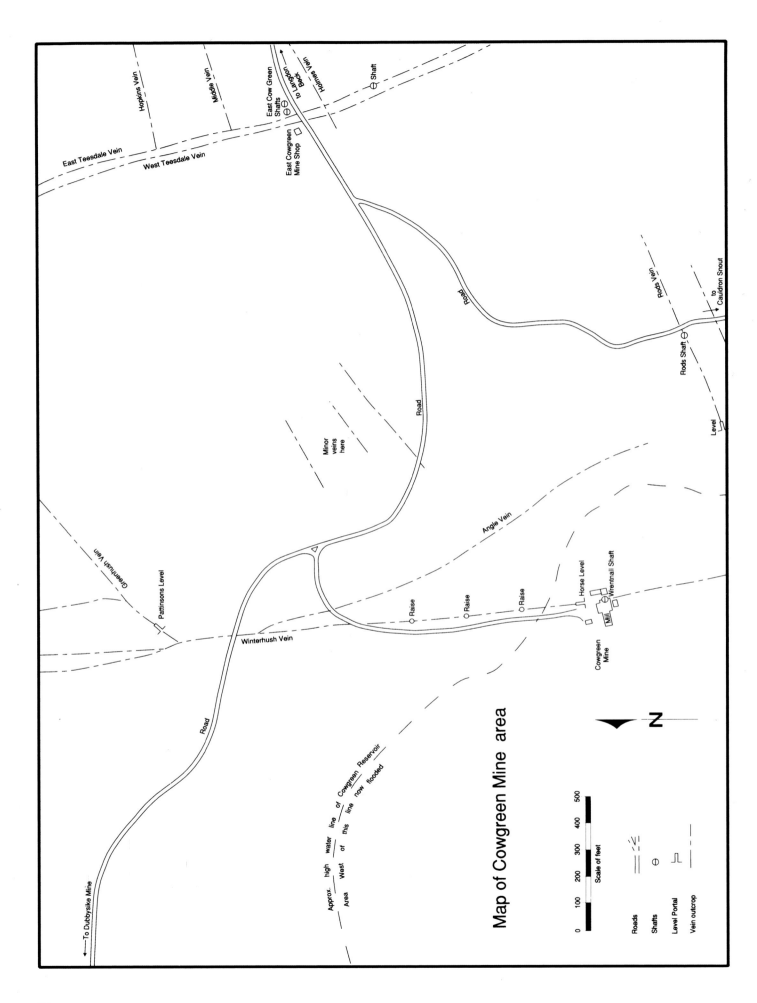

Map of Cowgreen Mine area

Hopkins Vein

Middle Vein

East Cow Green Shafts

Homes Vein

○ Shaft

East Teesdale Vein

West Teesdale Vein

East Cowgreen Mine Shop

to Langdon to Beck

Road

Road

Rods Vein

to Cauldron Snout

Rods Shaft ○

Level

Minor veins here

Angle Vein

Greenhush Vein

Pattinsons Level

Raise

Raise

Raise

Horse Level

Wrentnall Shaft

Winterhush Vein

Mill

Cowgreen Mine

Road

Approx. high water line of Cowgreen Reservoir

Area West of this line now flooded

To Dubbyske Mine

N

0   100   200   300   400   500

Scale of feet

Roads

Shafts ○

Level Portal

Vein outcrop

72

Cowgreen Mine, Wrentnall Shaft, 1950. Ernest Walton (Head Fitter) carrying the timber.

The crude ore was trammed along the working levels to the shaft area by ponies, who each pulled four mine cars at a time. They were very knowing beasts too, and if anyone tried to hang on an extra mine car they would refuse to budge. But in 1950 the ponies were superseded by battery electric locomotives.

At this time most of the work in the mine was set out on what was termed 'Contract', a form of incentive bonus scheme. The system involved a base rate for each job which was increased by a bonus payment which allowed for bonus rates for any surplus of ground broken or mine cars drawn above a fixed target per fortnight. In this way the miners could increase their wages by hard work, (or sometimes by good luck!). The contracts were set by the fortnight and the targets were agreed between the Mine Manager and the various partnerships, each side signing the agreement fortnightly. If the work was harder than expected or difficulties were encountered the partnerships

Wrentnall Shaft headframe, Cowgreen, 1950.

Train of empties entering Horse Level, Cowgreen, 1950.

Presently I looked at my watch and hurriedly got up. 'Eh Tommy', I said, 'I'd no idea it was so late, I must get along'. Before he could say more I got up and started to climb down the ladderway. The last I heard was Tommy shouting and swearing at me.

'Hey, Mister Smith, what about my price then'. A pause, then, 'By damn, he's done me again'.

As I said earlier, the haulage was done by ponies in my early days at Cowgreen and at the end of each working shift, those ponies which worked in the lower levels were brought to the surface in the cage and stabled for the night. There was one pony on the 106 ft level who always galloped away for a roll in the grass when he was let out of the cage and before he could be stabled and fed. One day I was looking out of the office window when I saw him gallop past and then start to rub himself against a three-inch diameter compressed air pipe which was on the hillside close to the office. As he pushed against the pipe a joint burst and with a roar of escaping air at both broken ends the pony, terrified by the sudden noise, galloped up the fellside like a racehorse. We did not catch him until the next day and some miles away from the mine. I do believe that, small though he was, he could almost have won the Derby that day. Life was never so exciting when we introduced locomotives.

Another incident concerning ponies occurred at about the same time as the above happening. The ponies were stabled in a building close to the shaft and the feed store next to the stable was infested with rats. We decided to have a clear-out one day and all the hay was removed, while several men stood by armed with pick shafts and when any rat ran out it was promptly clubbed down. There were some whoppers there too. As the rat hunt was in full swing, Ernie Walton, our Head Fitter happened to be passing and he thought this was good fun and he would join in, but he had hardly reached the place when a very large rat ran up his trouser leg. There was a loud yell and I have never seen a pair of overall trousers come off so quickly, nor anyone look quite so pale.

Snow was often a real problem at Cowgreen and sometimes in midwinter the road from the mine to Langdon Beck became badly blocked and the mine would be cut off for days on end. On these occasions we would set the whole mine crew to digging at the deep drifts; a most uncomfortable and tedious job at best. Even so we could often not get transport to the mine for some days and the pumpmen and hoistmen had to camp out there to keep the workings clear. Stores were kept at the mine for that purpose.

One day when there was quite a severe blizzard blowing, I was driving the mine Landrover up the road from Langdon Beck when I came upon a young couple walking up the road against the blinding snow. When I pulled up beside them I found that they were in shorts and wearing only plimsolls on their feet. I asked them where they thought they were going and what they were doing and they told me quite seriously that they were on a walking tour and were aiming to go to Cauldron Snout and from there to High Cup Nick and Appleby. I told them in no

were paid their base rates in any case, but if they had good luck and found easy going, or were extra industrious, the men could earn considerably more than their base rates. This system involved quite a bit of bargaining and knowledge of the mine by both sides, but on the whole it worked very well. However sometimes unexpected conditions made some difficulty and the Manager had power to increase a bargain price if he felt that it was fair to do so.

I can recall one Tommy Raine who was working a stope in the Greenhush Vein at the time and who felt that the price allotted to him was not sufficient, but I knew that this was not so and felt that it should stand as we had originally agreed. When I visited him one day in his stope he shouted angrily that he and his mate were not satisfied. Now I knew that Tommy was a very keen member of the Middleton Brass Band and before he could say more I smiled at him and said, 'Tommy I hear that you are all set to do very well in the band contest next week'.

He stopped for a moment, grinned at me and then started to tell me what the local band hoped to do in the contest and we carried on a very animated conversation for some minutes. He waxed very enthusiastic about his hopes.

The road to Cowgreen, winter 1950.

uncertain tones that they were mad and couldn't make it in such conditions. They were dressed for summer, not midwinter. So I made them get in with me and took them to the mine, where we gave them hot coffee and sent them back down the Dale on the next truckload of barytes. It is almost unbelievable what some folks will do.

It was often difficult to understand why people who lived outside the area failed to realise just how difficult conditions could be in upper Teesdale. Our head office was in Avonmouth and sometimes when the road was blocked by deep snow and we were unable to dispatch barytes from the mine I would receive frantic telephone calls complaining that no barytes had

Cow Green Mine, Wrentnall Shaft, 1950. The Austin Seven belonged to Charlie Robson, Chief Clerk, and a mainstay of the mine. The Bedford wagon belonged to the Beadle family. This firm transported the barytes to Middleton-in-Teesdale station.

Shaft on Rod's Vein, 1950.

been received at Widnes works. When I explained that the roads were impassable to the barytes trucks, they would say, 'But we have no snow here, it's quite mild'.

HM Inspectors of Mines were often dreaded by the mineworkers, though I always found them to be not only friendly, but also very helpful and understanding. After all they are all ex mine managers themselves and fully understand and sympathise with our problems. They often displayed humour as well. I can recall one Inspector named Stone, who visited us when we had reopened Dubbysike Mine, which was near Cowgreen and worked a wide vein in weak ground. The main stopes were about twenty feet wide and were kept filled with waste up to the working face. There were frequent ore chutes left timbered through the wastefill and these were open holes in the packed floor. As we walked through the stope I warned Mr Stone to be careful of these open holes.

'Oh', he remarked, 'If I fell down one of them it would only be like throwing an old stone down a hopper'.

On another occasion, when examining a development drift which was wet so that there were several inches depth of water on the floor of the level, I noticed a stick of dynamite floating in the water. I carefully put my foot over it and went on talking to the Inspector, but when we turned to leave the place the Inspector looked at me straight-faced and said quietly, 'I shouldn't tread too hard if I were you'.

Apart from the main mine worked at Cowgreen there were other veins in the large concession held by Anglo Austral Mines Ltd. from the Raby Estate. The concession in fact included almost the whole of Upper Teesdale.

Dubbysike Mine lies about one mile north of Cowgreen and was developed on a very powerful vein. It was opened in 1941, but had lain unworked until 1950, when it was reactivated and

produced a fair quantity of ore before the abandonment of the whole concession in 1952. There remain some fair prospects of further ore here, not explored as yet. Another vein was developed at Rod's Mine in 1950, where a shaft was sunk to a depth of 80 feet close to the road leading to Cauldron Snout. After producing some good ore from a narrow vein, it too was abandoned and little now remains of this working.

In 1950 it was decided that the lowest beds of the Carboniferous rocks should be explored to determine whether ore persisted in the lower parts of the Melmerby Scar Limestone and the basal beds. To this end Wrentnall Shaft was deepened to 315 feet below surface. At that depth the base of the Carboniferous was penetrated and the shaft entered the underlying Skiddaw Slates. Some exploration at this depth proved that the Winterhush Vein persisted down into the slates and was about five feet wide where proved. Unfortunately limited development there showed that the vein was filled mostly with calcite, with only traces of galena and pyrite, and was almost devoid of barytes. It was also very wet at that depth, with strong feeders of water.

Speaking of exploration I remember an interesting trial of dowsing which I made while at Cowgreen. One of our miners, Geordie Toward, was reputed to be a good dowser, so I took him to a place where I knew the ground was underlain by a vein, but where there was no outward sign of any working, and had him make several traverses across the ground. In each case he had a strong reaction at the right spots. I tried it myself with no result, but when Geordie took hold of one of the rods I could not stop them twisting in my hand at the same spots.

You may draw your own conclusions from that.

In 1952 it was decided that the mine was almost exhausted and the company abandoned the concession. The site was soon cleared and then lay abandoned until the Cowgreen reservoir was constructed, the dam being situated just to the north of Cauldron Snout waterfalls. The resulting lake has flooded the main mine site and so sterilised the whole area for mining purposes, so that any further work at the mines is unlikely.

Although the main mine site is under water now, some of the upper workings on Winterhush and Greenhush Veins may still be seen, though no underground exploration is now possible.

The closure of the mines was a sad occurrence for Upper Teesdale, as Cowgreen was the chief source of employment for the region and hill farming is now the only occupation for most of the Dalesfolk, apart from the whinstone quarry at High Force which remains at work to this day.

Relatively few of the miners of Cowgreen now remain with us, but for those who do the busy days there remain as happy memories of a very successful mine, which was described by the Orr's Zinc White Co.'s staff magazine in 1950, as... MINE ALONE.

All photographs by the author.

Thomas Walton's Trading Activities in Upper Weardale 1833–42

M C Tanner

Introduction

Thomas Walton was a native of Ireshopeburn and died at Low Burn in January 1855. Two of his notebooks have survived and they provide details of his lead mining interests and of his business as a provision merchant. A short article in *The Friends of Killhope Newsletter* (No. 32, January 1995) was based on material in one of the notebooks and summarised his activities in promoting and managing a number of small lead mines in the Garrigill area during the 1840s and early 1850s.

The other notebook is the source for the present article. It contains detailed information for the period 1833 to 1842 on Thos. Walton's provision merchant business. As such it provides background to the social and economic history of Upper Weardale which may not otherwise be available.

First of all who was he? Like many of his time he left behind an annotated family bible but placed himself at the apex of his family tree. His nine children are listed, as is the death of his wife Hannah (née Allison) in 1838. Subsequent generations have been added in different hands. His daughter-in-law, grandson, and great-grandson (the late John Harvey Walton, my father-in-law) were successive proprietors of the shop and post office at Cornriggs. Altogether this business survived for about 120 years after Thos. Walton's death in 1855.

Going back in time, he was born in August 1796 the first son of Thomas Walton (senr.) and became elder brother to ten other children. His father was a lead miner and lived successively at Ireshopeburn, Westfall, Balehill, Island House and Sedling Plain where he died in June 1832. His mother was born Ann Smith and she survived until June 1848, latterly at Low Burn.

Thomas Walton (senr.) was born in February 1767 the second son of Matthew Walton, then living at Hawkwellhead. Interestingly, although Matthew was (probably) born in October 1730 at St John's Chapel, he married Mary Watson at Alston in June 1759. She was the daughter of John Watson (of Stanhope parish) and Mary Dickinson, also of Alston. These details are significant because they support oral tradition among the Waltons that there was at one time a family connection with Alston. For the purposes of this note however they indicate that Matthew Walton, like his grandson Thomas, was accustomed to travel between Upper Weardale and Alston and, like many who did the same, was probably engaged in lead mining activities. He died at Blackcleugh in October 1788.

The Notebook

In the 1841 and 1851 census returns Thos. Walton is described as a general dealer and provision merchant respectively. These activities are reflected in the contents of his second notebook.

Cornriggs house and shop (alternatively known as Travellers' Rest) with a Walton family group photographed in 1897 or 1898.
(See page 88 for detail)   *Photograph: property of the author's family*

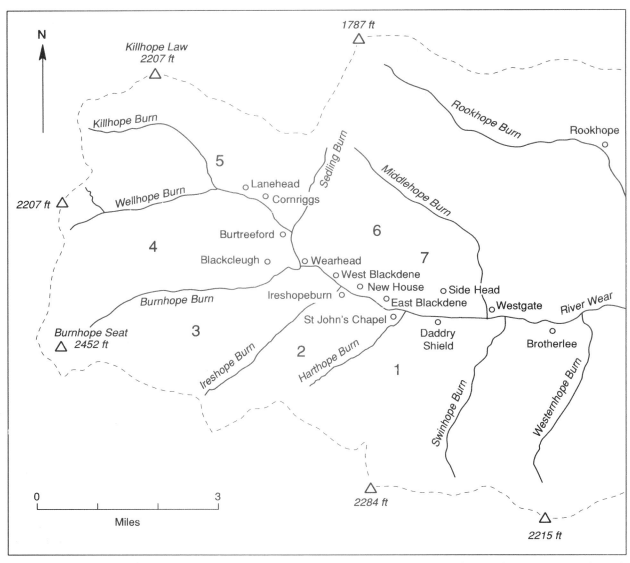

The 1841 census areas in Upper Weardale

Map based on 'Clearing the Forest', 1990, by kind permission of Peter Bowes

This is pocket sized, approximately 6¼ in x 4 in, containing originally about 230 numbered pages of which 35 are missing. There are extra unnumbered pages at the front and back. An almanac of correct stamp duties and dates of fairs is pasted onto the front flyleaf and the following two pages. This is followed by a home-made alphabetical index of customers (from which it is possible to deduce who was represented on the missing pages). The next 17 unnumbered pages record various transactions which for some reason did not find their way into the main part of the notebook, which follows. At the end there are 19 unnumbered pages recording other transactions, including deals in shareholdings of various non-lead mining enterprises.

The main body of the notebook covers the years 1833 to 1842. Of the 166 customers who are named, 159 are identified by habitation. A further 16 named customers can be inferred from the index but their habitations and records of their transactions have been lost on missing pages. The practice, to start with at least, was to allocate a whole page to each customer in turn. At the foot of each page the record overflowed to the next page not already occupied by a customer. Thus, for example, the record

for Ralph Humble of Lanehead starts at page 3, covering 1833 to 1835, continues to page 94 covering 1836 and 1837, and then goes to page 129 covering 1838 to 1840.

Internal evidence suggests that the records for each customer are summaries of more detailed information transcribed from ledger books now lost. Thus, typical entries are 'To goods, L book page 95', 'To monthly goods', 'Day book balance', 'Long book Back End', etc. Nevertheless enough individual items are recorded to allow something of the local economy to be reconstructed. Importantly, the summaries focus on the year-end debt incurred by each customer and the extent to which this was settled by cash payment.

The questions addressed in this article reflect two dimensions of a matrix, looking at the records from the point of view of Thos. Walton's business and then from the point of view of his customers.

The first set includes the number of customers on Thos. Walton's books, the total population he served, the turnover of his business, the extent of customer debt he carried and the source of the capital he needed to start and maintain his business. The second set overlaps the first and identifies the customers, what they did, what family they supported, how much they spent and what they spent it on, what they paid for individual items, whether they got into debt and, if so, how they managed.

As might be expected, answers are imprecise and subject to many qualifications but this article concludes with an attempt to place Thos. Walton's business in the context of the economy of Upper Weardale as a whole in the decade of the 1830s.

Lead Mining in Weardale during the 1830s

C. J. Hunt (*The Lead Miners of the Northern Pennines*) writes that the lead industry experienced a severe and long lasting depression in the early 1830s. The price of lead began to fall in the late 1820s, was below £15 per ton in 1832, recovered to £25 per ton in 1836 and thereafter hovered around £20 per ton. The London Lead Company's subsistence payments, normally 40*s*. per month around 1830, were made only to men working in good places and Hunt speculates that Blackett/Beaumont Co.'s subsistence payments, normally 30*s*. per month, may have been reduced in the early 1830s, although he concedes that there is no hard evidence for this.

Elsewhere Hunt summarises contemporary estimates of lead miners' annual earnings These were just over £18 in 1832, just under £21 in 1834, £32. 10*s*. in 1836 and had recovered to just over £39 (maximum) by 1842. It is against these estimates that the spends of most of Thos. Walton's customers have to be judged.

Thos. Walton's Customer Base

The 1841 census return for Stanhope Parish Forest Quarter (ignoring Rookhope, where Thos. Walton had only one recorded customer) followed a clockwise pattern, starting south of the Wear at Daddry Shield and St John's (1) and continuing west to include the area between Harthopeburn and Ireshopeburn (2), the area between Ireshopeburn and Burnhope Burn (3), the area between Burnhope Burn and Wellhope (4), the area at the head of the valley between Wellhope and Killhope Burn continuing north of the river through Lanehead to Cowshill (5), the area east of Sedling extending to Middle Blackdene (6) and finally the area between Middle Blackdene and Sidehead (7).

Of the 159 customers whose habitations are given, 101 were present as heads of households in the census return for these areas. These included 21 tradespeople, or at least people not engaged in lead mining (four blacksmiths, one butcher, two joiner/carpenters, two shoemakers, one mason, two farmers, three tailors, one saddler, one surgeon, one innkeeper, one sieve-bottom maker, one agricultural labourer and one illegible). Some of these households included lead miners.

The remaining 80 customers were either lead miners, or described as independent with households including lead miners.

The total customer population was estimated by adding in the number of dependants in each household. The number of additional wage-earners was also noted; generally these were sons employed as lead miners or, possibly, washer lads. The distribution between census areas of Thos. Walton's customer

population (assuming it was all on his books in 1841) is shown in the summary table below.

Census area	Customer population	Total population	% of total	Lead miners in Customer population	Lead miners in census area population	% of total
(1)	16	519	3.1	2	92	2.2
(2)	141	595	23.7	16	84	19.0
(3)	83	405	20.5	25	105	23.8
(4)	72	467	15.4	12	94	12.8
(5)	137	455	30.1	38	117	32.5
(6)	104	397	26.2	29	95	30.5
(7)	64	548	11.7	25	142	17.6
(All)	617	3386	18.2	147	729	20.2

This summary may understate the extent of Thos. Walton's business because it neglects 58 customers named in his book who, for one reason or another, did not appear in the census return. Six of these were resident outside the upper dale. For the rest, the family might have moved out of the census area by 1841, or the head of the household might have died. Even if, after such a loss, the family stayed put in the census area it cannot be securely correlated with any entry in the census return. The best extrapolated estimate would increase the above customer population by about a third (assuming again that it was all on his books in 1841).

On the other hand these estimates are unsatisfactory because not all of the identified people and their households were actually customers together in 1841 or indeed in any of the preceding 8 years. The situation is further complicated by the need to allow for customers believed to be represented on missing pages. The number of recorded customers (each taken to represent a household) in each year was as follows:

Year	As recorded	Corrected for missing pages
1833	45	46
1834	58	60
1835	56	60
1836	55	64
1837	62	71
1838	67	75
1839	70	78
1840	60	61
1841	32	32

At best, only 70 or so of the 101 recorded customers appear in any one year. It is clear from the detailed pattern that each year up to a score of new customers (and their households) were served by the business while others dropped out.

Most of Thos. Walton's business was concentrated in three areas. The largest group of his customer population and their dependants was around Ireshopeburn (2), where he lived and where most of his tradespeople customers and their families lived. Almost the same customer population was present in the Killhope to Lanehead area (5), amounting to 30 per cent of the census population there (or 40 per cent by extrapolation) and 32.5 per cent of the lead mining population (or 39 per cent by extrapolation). The third group was located north of the Wear between Wearhead and Middle Blackdene (6).

In 1841 almost all of the tradespeople were concentrated in census areas (1) and (2) with 83 persons in non-lead-mining occupations (ignoring male and female servants living-in). In the remaining five census areas there were only 72 persons in non-lead-mining occupations. There were no butchers west (or upstream) of Wearhead and no grocers west of Ireshopeburn/Middle Blackdene, but there were millers at Burtreeford. There were only two farmers (not apparently depending in any way on lead mining) in the stretch from Burnhopeburn running clockwise to Sedling (but it is known that lead mining families commonly had small-holdings).

In 1833, when Thos. Walton's transactions are first recorded, there could hardly have been more tradespeople in total and certainly no more upstream of Wearhead.

The tables raise several questions. Thos. Walton did business with, overall, only one fifth of the population. How was the rest served, particularly at the head of the dale, and who provided the service? Did the pattern of purchases differ between lead miners' families and tradespeople's families and were there differences in the way accounts were settled at the year end reflecting, perhaps, the number of dependants and the number of earners in the household?

Customers generally settled the past calendar year account during the first quarter of the next calendar year and most settlements followed the January pay day. This was the case both for lead miners and for tradespeople. The coincidence is to be expected because at this time new money would circulate rapidly from mine agent to miners to traders, who would then settle up between themselves.

For this analysis, all customer accounts were summarised on an annual basis and set down in spreadsheet form with customers on the vertical axis and years running horizontally. The annual summary comprised four items: (i) what the customer owed to the business at the year end (ii) what was paid (iii) the balance outstanding and (iv) interest on the outstanding balance (which Thos. Walton reckoned at 5 per cent p.a.). These items were summed for each of the 9 years for which customer records are available.

A prominent feature of these accounts is the extent of the debt incurred at year end by customers. Not all of his customers got into debt and, of those who did, not all seem to have had interest charged, or at least the interest due was not always recorded. Nevertheless the aggregate interest payable, based on what was recorded and added to the following year's accounts, averaged about £5 each year. The table below suggests that for most years about half of Thos. Walton's customers were in debt and some individuals remained in debt throughout the period.

Year	Recorded Customers	Customers in debt
1833	45	12
1834	58	19
1835	56	25
1836	55	33
1837	62	27
1838	67	28
1839	70	36
1840	60	30
1841	32	15

Hunt gives examples from Blackett/Beaumont sources of the extent of debt at Coalcleugh. In 1831, during the depression, a hundred and twenty three men owed money but by 1836, in more prosperous times, only seven owed money. These debts were of course to the company; tradespeople were further down the chain and Thos. Walton's experience suggests that they had to carry debts for longer periods. However his interest charges were only 5 per cent rather than the exorbitant 30 per cent to 35 per cent p.a. as was estimated by Sopwith and quoted by Hunt.

The example below shows how one individual was unable to pay for goods supplied in 1836 and was charged 7s. 6d. interest. He offset his debt during 1837 by harvesting and providing hay valued at 16s. and eventually cleared all his debt by mid 1838.

The aggregate debt is shown in the summary table below (with sums rounded to the nearest old penny).

Year	Owed to the Business			Paid to the Business			Outstanding Balance		
	£.	s.	d.	£.	s.	d.	£.	s.	d.
1833	166	15	1	114	18	7	51	16	0
1834	220	2	8	150	5	7	69	8	5
1835	283	12	7	153	6	10	119	5	2
1836	365	5	10	144	3	0	204	5	5
1837	381	9	5	183	2	6	163	1	3
1838	349	13	7	197	11	11	129	18	7
1839	332	10	0	155	4	6	176	5	6
1840	291	3	7	130	3	11	147	16	10
1841	198	11	5	77	10	6	105	5	5

Discrepancies in the table arise because Thomas Walton occasionally wrote off minor debts such as the odd penny or so.

More importantly, some transactions are incomplete in that sums owing are not balanced by records of sums paid, or recorded debts are not accompanied by entries of sums previously owed and paid. The best that can be claimed, in view of these discrepancies, is that the annual totals for sums owed, sums paid, and outstanding debts were at least as big as the values in the table.

The sums owed to the business (above) are not a proper measure of the actual turnover in goods. A better estimate is obtained by subtracting the outstanding balance at the start of one year from what was owed at the end of that year:

Year	Turnover in goods			Number of Customers	Average per Customer		
	£.	s.	d.		£.	s.	d.
1833	166	15	1	45	3	14	2
1834	168	6	9	58	2	18	1
1835	214	4	2	56	3	16	6
1836	246	0	8	55	4	9	6
1837	177	4	0	62	2	17	2
1838	186	12	5	67	2	15	8
1839	202	11	6	70	2	17	11
1840	114	18	1	60	1	18	4
1841	50	14	8	32	1	11	9

The table above assumes that no debt was outstanding prior to 1833 and that the data for 1841–42 are reliable in spite of the generally scattered nature of the entries for that year. It seems either that the business was in decline after 1840, surprisingly in view of the recovery in the lead mining industry, or that Thos. Walton was deliberately running down this particular activity. This possibility is discussed further in the postscript to this article.

Hunt quotes a range of sources showing that some three-quarters of a lead mining family's income was spent on food. If this was so then in the period 1833 to 1841 one would expect to find customer annual average spends in the range £15 to £25, if they were with a single supplier. Clearly they were not. We have to conclude therefore that Thos. Walton only supplied perhaps one fifth of the requirements of those households (about a fifth of the total) which were on his books.

The average of 61 recorded annual spends in the tradespeoples' group was £2. 4s. 2d. with only a 1 in 20 chance of a spend exceeding £4. 5s. 6d. The mean of 260 recorded annual spends in the lead miners' group was £3. 3s. 2d. with a 1 in 20 chance of the spend exceeding £6. The difference between these two averages is statistically very significant.

The most likely explanation for the difference is that tradespeople would generally be able to provide for their own needs, either for free or at least at cost. This reasoning would perhaps apply well to grocers, butchers and shoe makers (but is difficult to apply, for example, to blacksmiths). Moreover tradespeople, as noted, were concentrated mostly in census areas (1) and (2) where there was a choice available between several traders supplying some or all of the goods and services offered by Thos. Walton. Such customers could conveniently spread their business between several suppliers, spending on average comparatively little with each. We know nothing of the loyalty of customers to their suppliers but in these areas, and possibly (3), customers could easily visit fixed shops and use the opportunity to compare prices.

On the other hand the lead mining group, particularly in the Killhope–Lanehead census area (5), would have very restricted opportunities for visiting shops. While there must have been other suppliers visiting the area (Thos. Walton had at most only one third of the customer base there) it is not difficult to imagine the convenience that customers might find in remaining loyal to a single supplier; for example in agreeing what was to be delivered in the next order, and when and, most importantly, agreeing terms for credit. This is not to say that competition between suppliers did not occur; each new customer would need to make an initial choice based on reputation, the range of goods on offer, their price, convenience of the delivery schedule and credit terms.

Lead miners' spends with Thos. Walton in each of the 7 census areas show significant differences between areas.

Census area	Number of recorded spends	Average spend		
		£.	s.	d.
(1)	6	2	2	10
(2)	31	3	11	11
(3)	32	2	14	4
(4)	24	1	7	4
(5)	107	3	5	7
(6)	40	2	13	11
(7)	20	4	17	4

These data add little to the interpretation given above. The average for area (1) may be disregarded because of the narrow data base.

Prices charged for goods and commodities
Food.

1833	New cheese	6½d.	per lb
	Ordinary cheese [?]	3d.	per lb
	Bacon	6d.	per lb
	Beef	6s.	per stone
		(5d.	per lb)
1834	New cheese	6½d. to 7d.	per lb
	Maslin [rye and wheat mix]	1s. 8d. to 1s. 9d.	per stone
	Sugar	7d.	per lb
1835	Bacon	7s. 6d.	per stone
		(6½d.	per lb)
1837	Coffee	2s.	per lb
	Tea	5s. 6d.	per lb
	Cheese [new?]	8d. to 8½d.	per lb
	Sugar	9½d.	per lb
1838	Ordinary cheese [?]	4d.	per lb
	Butter	10½d.	per lb
	[provided in payment for goods]		
	Sugar	8d.	per lb
	Flour	3s. 2d.	per stone
		(2¾d.	per lb)
	1 side [beef or bacon]	7s. 6d.	per stone
		(6½d.	per lb)
	Potatoes	6d.	per stone
1839	Sugar	5½d.	per lb
	1 side [beef?]	7s. 10d.	per stone
	Cheese [new?]	7½d.	per lb
	Ham	8s. 11d.	per stone
		(7½d.	per lb)
1840	Flour	2s. 9d. to 2s. 10d.	per stone
	Sugar	10d.	per lb
	Raisins	3d.	per lb
1841	Ham	8s. 10d.	per stone
	Tea	5s. 6d.	per lb
	Flour	2s. 8d. to 2s. 9d.	per stone

Thos. Walton was renting about 4 acres of grassland near Low Burn in 1841 and had a share in a 30-acre allotment a mile to the south-west of the village. He would use this to provision his horses but may also have raised cattle and pigs for slaughter. It is therefore possible that his notebook entries for sides of beef or bacon were wholesale prices.

Hunt's sources state that maslin bread was the main food in Weardale in 1834 and that rye bread appears to have been forsaken shortly after 1841, being replaced by barley which was still the main breadstuff of the lead mining community as late as the 1870s. Wheaten bread is scarcely mentioned in any of Hunt's sources. These observations raise questions about the nature of the flour recorded in Thos. Walton's notebook.

Wheat in the 1830s was about twice as expensive as barley, which in turn was about half as much again as oats. Hunt's sources suggest that rye was less expensive than barley in the latter half of the eighteenth century but that by the turn of the century both rye and maslin had become more expensive than barley. The best guess is that Thos. Walton's flour was in fact derived from barley.

Clothing

1833	Pair of spats	3s. 1½d.	
	Worsted shawl	4s. 3d.	
	Silk handkerchief	4s. 3d.	
	Indian handkerchief	4s.	
	Handkerchief	3s. 3d.	
	Pair trousers	16s. 3d.	
	Blankets	6s. and 6s. 6d.	
	Jacket	7s.	
	Cloth	5s. per yard	
	Harding	11d. per yard	
1834	Hats	7s. 6d., 14s., and 14s. 6d.	
	Yarn	2s. for 9 oz	
1835	Cord cotton waistcoat	9s. 1d.	
	Ribbon	2d per yard	
1836	Umbrella	5s.	
	Gloves	1s. 3d.	
1837	Ticking	9d. per yard	
1838	Harden	10½d. per yard	
1839	Clogs	3s. 6d. per pair	
	Red-grey cloth	3s. per yard	
1840	Umbrella	5s. 6d.	
1841	Harden	1s. 2d. per yard	

There are 7 recorded sales of harden or harding. The OED (1964) says harden (or hurden) is a coarse fabric made from hards (or hurds), which in turn are the coarser parts of flax or hemp. Websters New International Dictionary (1934) agrees and goes on to say that the word is (or was) Scottish and dialect English; it seems appropriate that the word should surface in Upper Weardale in the 1830s. Happily, Thos. Walton's own dictionary (believed to have been printed between 1791 and 1794 and described in its preface as the first work of its kind that had been attempted in Scotland) gives hards as the 'refufe or coarfer part of flax'. The fabric seems generally to have retailed at about 11d. per yard.

Coal

In total the records cover delivery of 126 cart loads of coal, distributed among about 40 customers over 7 years. Prices seem to have risen slightly during the period but there are irregularities (e.g. one customer was charged 11s. and 12s. for successive deliveries during 1838, and different customers paid different amounts for deliveries on the same date) suggesting that Thos. Walton took into account what he had to pay wholesale and the distance over which he had to deliver. Thus at Earnwell, his base, at the east end of Ireshopeburn cart-loads were 9s. 6d. in 1834, 10s. in 1836 and 1837, and 11s. in 1838, 1839 and 1840. At Lanehead they were 10s. 6d. in 1834, 11s. 6d. in 1836 and 12s. in 1838. Deliveries to Killhope were 12s. in 1836 and 12s. 6d. in 1837.

The weight of coal in each delivery is not known for certain, but it was probably carried in the 'small cart' described by Alan Blackburn (Men, Mines & Minerals of the North Pennines, 1992) as in common use for moving coal, lime and peat. It would hold 1 bing (8 cwt) of lead ore or 110 stones (12 cwt) of smelted lead. On two occasions single sacks (1 cwt) of coal were sold for 1s., consistent with the inference that a cart-load was 10 cwt or half a ton. On this basis Thos. Walton's selling price was about the same per ton as the average price of coals (from the north-east) at the ships' side in London.

Just as Thos. Walton only served between one fifth and one third of the total population in the upper dale, depending on location, so his customers for coal were only one quarter of the total on his books. Moreover not all of these took the kind of regular delivery absorbed for example by the Stephenson household at Earnwell, averaging 44 cwt per year. How did everyone else keep themselves warm? Were there other coal merchants operating in the area or did most of the population rely wholly or in part on their rights to crow coal or peat?

Miscellaneous

1833	Two letters	1s. 7d.	
1834	Funeral	£2 10s. 11d.	
	[charge to John Robson]		
1835	Funeral	£1 11s. 3d.	
	[charge to Jos. Peart]		
	Liquor	4s. 7½d.	for 37 gallons
[possibly used in smithying and not alcoholic]			
1836	Oats	5s. 6d.	per bushel
	Winning hay	16s.	
	[payment by Wm. Rumney]		
	Hay		8d. per stone supplied
1837	Meal	£1 2s. 6d.	per bushel
	Glazing	£1 8s. 6d.	[unspecified]
1839	Carriage	2s.	
	for 8 stones of potatoes		
1840	Leather	3d.	per stone
	Two stints of grass	£1 6s. 0d.	
	[paid by Wm. Rumney]		
	Bag of nails	4d.	
	Chairs	5s. 6d.	each
	Armchair	7s. 6d.	
	Carriage of chairs	1s. 6d.	
	1 stint in the pasture	13s.	
	[charged to Thos. Brown]		
1841	Carriage of leather from Carlisle	1s. 6d.	for 43 stones
	Carriage of beef	3s.	for 12 stones
	Hay	5½d.	per stone
	[supplied by J. Heatherington]		

Early Mining Speculation

Thos. Walton's lead mining activities summarised in *The Friends of Killhope Newsletter* (No. 32, Jan. 1995) postdate the provision merchant transactions discussed so far. He may have developed a taste for mining speculation in 1839. A complex sequence of transactions related to the purchase and almost immediate sale of shares in various (non-lead) mining enterprises is recorded in that year in the unnumbered pages at the back end of the pocket book. The story is set out in Thos. Walton's words.

Thos Walton bought the folowing shares of an Iorn [Iron ?] mine on Scarrowmanwick fell, in the parish of Kirkoswald in the County of Cumberland, held in grant under George Musgrave Bart. Eden Hall.

1839		£.	s.	d.
May 4	1/32 share of Adam Bell	2	15	0
Jun 1	1/32 share of Adam Bell	3	0	0
Jun 8	1/32 share of Rodger Lightbown	5	0	0
Jun 15	1/32 share of Thos. Eddy	8	0	0
Jun 15	1/32 share of Thos. Henderson	4	0	0
Jun 22	1/16 share of Thos. Eddy	10	0	0
	[total for 7/32 shares]	32	15	0
	[Unspecified purchase, possibly barytes and sulphur mines below]	30	0	0
	[total]	62	15	0

1839 Thos Walton Bought of Blagill Barytes Mine		£.	s.	d.
June 10	Adam Bell 1/32 share for	5	0	0
-do- 10	paid in cash	5	0	0
June 10	Bought of Thos Eddy 1/32 share of the [same?] mine for the sum of	5	0	0
-do- 10	Paid in cash	5	0	0
June 10	Bought of Thos Eddy and Adam Bell 1/32 share of Tyne Head Sulphur Mine and [likewise ?] 1/32 share of Blagill Barytes Mine	19	19	0
-do- 10	By cash	19	19	0
Sold In the said Ion [iron?] Mine				
June 11	to John Allison 1/64 share	5	0	0
-do- 11	to Thos Peart [1/64 share ?]	5	0	0
-do- 17	to Thos Peart 1/32 share	30	0	0
-do- 22	to John Greaves 1/32 share	8	0	0
	to Harrison Barnfather 1/64 share	15	0	0
	to John Allison 1/64 share	15	0	0
July 12	to John Heatherington 1/32 share	30	0	0
Our Bargin Share of Barytes				
	Ralph Allison 1/32 share	20	0	0
	Robt Baxter 1/64 share	Not taken up		
1839 Thomas Walton received cash for shares of Ion [Iron ?] mine				
June 11	John Allison	5	0	0
	Harrison Barnfather	15	0	0
-do- 22	John Greaves	8	0	0
-do- 25	Received of Thos Peart	20	0	0
July 22	John Allison	10	0	0
July 26	Received of Thos Peart which paid in full for 1/16 of the Ion [?] mine	30	0	0
	[total]	88	0	0

	£	s	d
1839 Mr Thos Peart, Gold Hill Dr to Thos Walton	50	0	0
June 25 For one 1/16 share of an Ion [?] mine in the parish of Kirkoswald received in cash	20	0	0
Balance	30	0	0
July 26 By cash [from] Thomas Peart	30	0	0
1839			
Nov 11 Thos Walton Recd. of John Heatherington for the Ion [?] mine	14	0	0
for Wilkinson [Williamson ?]	4	0	0
[total]	18	0	0
1840			
Feb 3 Received	15	0	0

From the above it appears that Thomas Walton obtained 7/32 shares in the Iron Mine for £32. 15s. 0d., 3/32 shares in the Barytes Mine for £15 and 1/32 shares in the Sulphur Mine for £15, a total layout of £62. 15s. 0d. in mid-1839. He tried to sell 5/32 shares of the Iron Mine for £108 and finished up receiving £103, possibly still holding 2/32 shares. In addition he seems to have agreed to sell 1/32 shares in the Barytes Mine for £20 but it is not certain that he got his money. It is not clear what became of his shares in the Sulphur Mine.

Source of Funds for Business

This sequence of deals could presumably only get off the ground if Thos. Walton was able to put cash down for shares in these mines. He was prepared to borrow for this purpose (and may have been doing so anyway to launch and sustain his provision merchant business). His notebook records debts and progress made in their discharge. Most of his obligations were cleared by 1842 but curiously he allowed one quite modest debt to run on up to 1847, paying 10s. interest per year. His words again:

	£.	s.	d.
Thos Walton Borrowed of John Rippon	50	0	0
1840 May 13 Interest with cash paid	20	0	0
Leaving balance	30	0	0
1841 Mar 26 By cash paid	15	0	0
Balance left	15	0	0
Sept 13 One ham 1 stone 11 lb @ 9s. per St.		16	0
Balance left	14	4	0
Dec 18 By cash	10	0	0
Balance left	4	4	0
1842 Feb 1 One cheese 11 lb @ 7d per lb.		6	5
Balance left	3	17	7
Oct 31 Settled the above and paid £1. 2s. 5d. interest	3	17	7
Thos Walton Dr. to John Allison			
1837 Apr 23	40	0	0
Interest paid			
1841 Jan 23 By cash	23	0	0
Balance left	17	0	0
-do- May 8 Interest paid			
1842 May [?] Interest paid			
-do- Aug 11 To goods supplied	1	8	9
Balance left	15	11	3
By cash paid	15	11	3
1834 Apr 24 Thos Walton Borrowed of John Hill	30	0	0
1841 May 10 Paid of the above sum	20	0	0
Balance left	10	0	0
1841 Interest not paid	1	10	0
Interest on ten pounds		10	0
Sum outstanding	12	0	0

	£.	s.	d.
1842 Feb 21 Cash to Mrs Hill	12	0	0
Paid Mr George Gardner Interest of up to the present due	20	0	0
1841 Jan 23 with	10	0	0
of the above sum leaving a balance of	10	0	0
1842 paid 10/- interest			
1843 Jan -do- 10/- -do-			
1844 Jan -do- 10/- -do-			
1845 Feb 3 paid 10/- interest			
1847 Jan interest paid up to January			

One unnumbered page summarises interest payments to creditors for 1838, 1839 and 1840. There are signs that the summary was intended to include 1841 but the task must have been interrupted These entries are consistent with the detailed listing of payments to individuals above.

Interest payments at 5 per cent
Thos Walton paid 1 years interest

1838		£.	s.	d.
May 10	George Heatherington	5	0	0
May 19	John Hill interest 1 year	1	10	0
May 12	Joh. Allison -do- -do-	2	0	0
1839				
Mar 4	paid George Gardner	1	0	0
May 12	paid John Hill's wife	1	10	0
Jun 11	paid George Heatherington	5	0	0
	paid Joh. Allison	2	0	0
Sept 6	paid Mr John Rippon	2	10	0
1840				
Jan 31	George Gardner	1	0	0
Jun 8	paid John Hill	1	10	0
	paid Joh. Allison	?		
1841	?	?		

The transactions on the page above show how, early in 1842, John Heatherington offset his debt of £9. 0s. 7½d. for sundry goods by providing nearly three-quarters of a ton of hay valued at £2. 12s. 11d. He then received £3. 12s. 3½d. in cash from Thos. Walton which brought his debt up to exactly £10: this balanced the interest due to him over two years on an outstanding loan of £100 and thus for the time being all obligations were settled between them. It is noteworthy that Thos. Walton paid interest of £5 to George Heatherington in 1838 and 1839, and the same amount to John Heatherington in 1842 so the loan was a long standing one. Is it possible that this is the same Heatherington who was persuaded to buy shares in the Scarrowmanwick iron mine in 1839?

Thos. Walton possibly held, and certainly rented, land. Payment of £5. 15s. 0d. to Ann Whitfield for 6 months rent is recorded in 1839 and a whole year's rental for field and pasture, £11. 10s. 0d., was paid to Nicholas Whitfield in 1840. Rental payments for land or property of £12 and £17 were made in 1841 and 1842 to Thos. Emerson Esq. of Frosterley and a note records that the account had been settled up to May 1842. Payments of land tax to Thos. Emerson are recorded in 1840 (3s. 3d.) and 1842 (1s. 6d.) but one or both of these may have been on behalf of Thos. Peart.

On the other hand grazing land was let to Josuah Dawson whose payments in return are recorded in 1838, 1841 and 1842.

Received of Mr Josuah Dawson		£.	s.	d.
1838 Jany. 30	for grass.			
	Four and three quarters stints		1	8	6
	Paid Isaac Dawson for hirding			11	8
	Balance			16	10

Josuah Dawson (Irestone) Dr to Thos Walton			£.	s.	d.
1841 May 23	Four and three quarters stints			1	6	0
	Received the above			1	6	0
	One cow bulled	paid			2	6
1842 Feb 22	Received of Josuah Dawson					
	Four and threequarters stints			1	6	0
	Two cows bulled				5	0
	Settled					

Thos. Brown occupied Low Burn at the west end of Ireshopeburn in 1841 and according to the 1841 tithe map was joint tenant with Thos. Walton of 30 acres of grazing land to the south-west of Ireshopeburn. The adjacent page shows how in each of the years 1840 and 1841 they shared the cost of hirding by paying Isaac Dawson 11s. 8d. Thos. Walton also paid 13s. each year for a stint in the pasture.

Thos. Walton moved from Earnwell to Low Burn some time between 1841 and 1848, possibly after the death of Thos. Brown who was aged 75 in 1841.

Elsewhere there are cryptic entries relating to schooling and provision of papers.

Received of Whit Dawson for papers		£.	s.	d.
1839 Nov 14	Cash		13	0
1841	One and a half years paid			
	from the above date		1	19	6
1842 May 7	Due 1 and ½ year		1	19	6
1842 Nov 14	Due for papers		2	12	0
	By cash			18	6
	School		1	13	6
Childrens schooling paid to January 29 1843			2	12	0

In 1841 Thos. Walton's children still in education would probably be Hannah (12), Jane (10), Phillis (8) and Thomas (6). Sarah (3) would perhaps be too young and Margaret (15), John (15) and Mary (14) would be too old.

It is not clear which school the children attended. The Newhouse school did not open until 1852 so they would have gone either to the Wearhead or St John's Chapel Barrington schools. Here the 'quarter pence' rate was 1s. 6d. per child (T. A. Milburn, 1987) and fees for one and a half years for 4 children would total £1. 16s. 0d. which agrees very nearly with the notebook record. It seems that Thos. Walton supplied papers (possibly legal paper: scholars would surely be using slates at this time!) for which payment by Whit. Dawson was partly in cash and partly by provision of schooling.

A revealing but undated entry reads:

'John English Dr. to Thos. Walton when put in prison at Northallerton his father got the money to see him £1. 8s. 5d.'

Transactions for 1837 were summarised as below

1837		£.	s.	d.
Jan 25	received of John Hodgson for grass		14	0
	received of John Fairless for grass		14	0
1837	paid Jos Joplin[g]	6	10	0
	paid John Gill coals		10	0
	Jos Walton Sedling	5	0	0
	paid John Philipson		13	6
	paid Ann Whitfield	5	15	0
	paid Philipson and Teasdale	2	16	8½

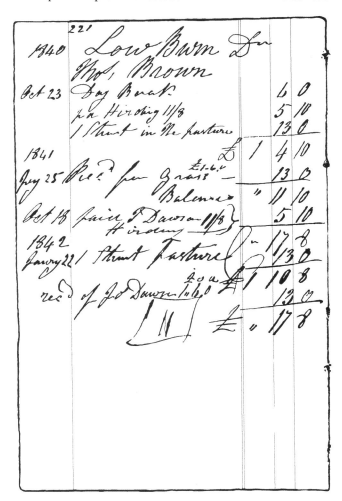

1837		£	s	d
	paid John Grean	7	0	0
	paid Oragone [?]	2	10	0
	paid Mr Muschamp	7	0	0
	paid Mr Morland	17	0	0
	paid Miller carrier	2	0	0
	paid Ellison [?] Penrith	4	14	0
	paid Oliver Durham	2	6	0
	paid Stanley Wilkinson	15	0	0
	paid Ralph Watson	20	0	0
	paid Daniel Pots	7	14	0
	paid Wilm. Pots	12	0	0
	paid Mr Hall Wolsingham	1	0	0
	paid Mr Reavely Featherstone	20	0	0
	paid Mr Norman	17	10	0
1837	Jan 31 [total]	155	9	2½

These look like payments to wholesalers, creditors and landlords at the end of the 1836–7 year. The tables shown

superimposed on a much more complex web of transactions. These occurred between tradespeople, miners and farmers (some individuals were all three) and covered loans, interest payments on loans and outstanding debts, rent, provision of forage, buying and selling of shares in small mines and the purchase of tradeable goods and miscellaneous services.

Thos. Walton seems to have been in the thick of all these deals. He was responsible for large sums in cash, his business carried large debts and he managed several personal loans. His notebook shows evidence of the care with which he kept track of all these affairs but unfortunately provides almost no clue as to how he got started. He raised a large family and saw to it that they got the schooling that he must have had earlier on. He had a wide range of customers and suppliers and must have been known to many more in the upper dale. He seems to have been prosperous by the standards of his time and place.

Enlargement of Walton family group shown on page 79. The gentleman is John Walton, grandson of Thomas Walton. The author's father-in-law Harvey Walton is standing third from the left at the back: he would then be aged 12 or 13. His mother, seated with a child, was born Phoebe Featherstone.   Photograph: property of the author's family.

earlier in this article indicate that Thos. Walton's business turnover in that year was strictly about £246, although only £144 was paid to the business while £365 was owed to the business. These figures illustrate the need for borrowing to provide working capital, and they suggest (if the list above is complete) that Thos. Walton anticipated a surplus for the year of around £90 We cannot say how representative this single estimate may be, but, based on Hunt's sources, it is approaching three times a lead miners earnings at the time.

These examples show how the simple picture of subsistence payments from mine owners to lead miners, and from them to tradespeople in payment for the necessities of life, has to be

Postscript

It has already been noted that the number of Thos. Walton's customers, and the average turnover per customer, declined in 1841 to about half of their values five years earlier in spite of the pick-up in the lead industry in the late 1830s. This may reflect a deliberate attempt on his part to run down the delivery of provisions and to concentrate on other business matters. What follows is no more than plausible speculation but it links the available facts with contemporary trends in the industrial and social history of Weardale.

For example, Hunt notes that the altitude of the lead mining dales largely prohibited the growing of vegetable food. Much

Nevertheless Slater's 1848 Durham Directory includes Thos. Walton of Ireshopeburn in the listing of grocers, dealers and drapers. He was also in business as a carrier, running carts to Alston every Saturday and to Bishop Auckland every Thursday, although the extension of the Stockton and Darlington Railway to Frosterley in the previous year must have affected this activity. All this was on top of his lead mining interests.

By 1848 Thos. Walton had moved to Low Burn with his two youngest daughters and in the 1851 census he was described as a provision merchant with three menservants in his household. The same census shows his eldest son, John, with his wife Margaret (née Dixon) and two infants, in a separate establishment at Low Burn. He was described as a draper and grocer but it is not known whether he ran a fixed shop or continued the itinerant carrier tradition.

Ominously, in view of the likely arrangements for water supply and sanitation at that time, the census records a total of 97 people, half of them children, in 22 families all at the Low Burn address. John Walton died in August 1854 and Thos. Walton in January 1855, both of typhoid.

Thos. Walton's Will was signed and witnessed only a week before he died. This is what it says;

'This is the last Will of me Thomas Walton Provision Merchant of Low Burn Weardale. After my decease I direct a valuation of the Stock; Book Debts; Hay; Corn; Furniture; Plate and all other articles belonging to me at Low Burn; Travellers Rest and elsewhere. I direct 2 of the horses, 2 carts with harnefs and gear to be sold, I direct 2 horses and 2 carts to be kept with their harnefs and gear and I also desire that my faithful servant Thomas Dawson be continued in the place he has long been employed in under me. If £400 can be obtained for [my] Netherhurth Lead Mine shares let them be sold. My 5/64 of Howgill 2/32 of North Nattrafs and shares of Dryburn Lead Mines to be parted with at such prices as can be realised. I bequeath to my son Thomas Two Hundred pounds for himself with which to carry on the house and businefs in the Premises now occupied by me and that my Daughter in Law Margaret Walton with her five children continue in the house and live with him in the same manner they have done with me. I bequeath to my daughter Sarah Forty Pounds and to Margaret and Mary my two married daughters Thirty Pounds each. I direct all my liabilities to be first paid. I appoint Benjamin Wren of Yarm, William Bennington of Stockton and John Elliot of Travellers Rest Executors to this my Will. etc. etc.'

Slaters 1848 and 1855 directories record that William Bennington and Co. was a wholesale grocery business located at 39 High Street, Stockton on Tees. It is likely that both Wren and Bennington were able to do business with Thos. Walton by

Margaret Walton (née Dixon), daughter-in-law of Thomas Walton and mentioned in his will. The date of the photograph is unknown but it may have been connected with the wedding of her son John Walton in 1881. *Photograph: property of the author's family.*

of it, and all cereals, had to be imported from arable areas elsewhere. During the eighteenth century the major lead mine owners were intermittently responsible for such importation and the mechanics of this operation would be part of local tradition and visible to Thos. Walton in his youth. What more natural than that as an adult he should seek to exploit a niche as a carrier and to deliver provisions on his own account?

However the improvement of turnpikes during the 1820s and development of railways elsewhere in County Durham in the 1830s meant that goods could more easily be got into the dale. It is also possible that by 1841 individual customers were tending to favour fixed shops offering a greater range of wares. They were certainly mobile: Mitchell's 1842 report talks of Weardale lead miners travelling on Saturdays to the nearest pit on the edge of the coal country to return with cart-loads of fuel.

virtue of the connection afforded by the Stockton and Darlington Railway as far as Frosterley.

Travellers Rest was evidently part of Thos. Walton's estate: his widowed daughter-in-law Margaret and her young family moved there, possibly in 1856. All three of her sons became lead miners but the two eldest and their families emigrated to New Zealand with many others on the Margaret Galbraith in 1879. She continued a grocery and drapery business at Cornriggs for nearly thirty years before handing over to her youngest son John Walton in 1884. Margaret Walton, the last person in the family to have known Thos. Walton, died in 1897 and was known universally as 'Peggy-od-Rest'.

Notebook page illustrations have been computer-processed to maintain their readability through the printing processes.

An Outline of the History and Industrial Archaeology of the Flotation Process for Mineral Separation

C C Short

Introduction

Traditional ore separation techniques relied almost exclusively on gravity separation; indeed what was not gravity separation was hand picking! Yet today, whereas gravity operations are not entirely superseded, the most common ore separation process is flotation, almost the exact opposite of gravity methods. The Broadwood plant built by Swiss Aluminium, UK, at Frosterley utilised flotation alongside gravity separation processes.

(In this attempt to describe the principle of the process do not worry if it remains unclear; as the early processes are described it should become clearer.) Described simply, the process relies on 'wetting'. Wetting is the extent to which a liquid embraces a material in contact with it. Different materials are wetted to different extents, and a material will be rejected by a liquid if it is not wetted by it. The pond skater skips to and fro on top of a water surface by a similar phenomenon. Oil and water do not wet each other, and separate, the oil floating because it has a lower density than water.

If it is possible to arrange that a desired ore is selectively wetted by a certain liquid, but not the gangue, then the unwetted gangue will not appear in that liquid. If equipment can be developed to extract the liquid which contains the ore, you have a very efficient separation process. This is the basis of the original flotation process, which used oil as the wetting agent, in water. Improvements have turned it round, so that the unwanted material is wetted and the unwetted ore is floated off. The process is developed to the stage of preferential flotation, being able almost at will to extract the ores wanted, and with recovery rates of over 92 per cent.

1. The Legend – and more prosaic observations

The development of the flotation process is generally ascribed to the Elmore brothers, and thanks to the accounts of the Elmores and their associates, popular mining history has established the story as legend. Francis Edward and Alexander Stanley Elmore were born in Liverpool on the 9th November, 1864, and the 1st January, 1867, respectively. By 1889 they were joint owners with their father William of an electrolytic copper refining and copper tube manufacturing operation in Leeds.

In 1896 William Elmore and some associates purchased a poor copper mine at Glasdir, some three miles north of Dolgellau in north Wales. The operation was having trouble recovering copper pyrites with a water based gravity separation mill, largely because of the small density difference between the ore and the gangue. Then it was noticed that at two places where accidental splashing of the slurry onto oil or grease had occurred, a clear deposit of pyrites, *without any gangue material present* was found. The oil was wetting the pyrites, and holding it in place, but not the gangue, which was being flushed away. From this, so the account goes, the momentous discovery of wetting was made, and as a result of much

experimentation, the first flotation plant was built at Glasdir.

There is truth in the account, and the Glasdir work did herald effective wetting and flotation technology, but the legend fails to take note of earlier discoveries. The ancient Greeks were employing wetting technology when they used feathers dipped in pitch to recover gold from alluvial mud deposits. In 1860 a patent had been taken out to use oil and water to recover ore adhering to parts of gravity separation equipment, and in 1866 reagents were patented using the same technology for washing ore-impregnated clothes. In 1877, in Bavaria, oil was used to float out graphite using gas bubbles, an anticipation of later developments. Even at Glasdir, a previous owner had sought in 1892 to use oil as a means of separating the pyrites, although without success. The failure of this venture occasioned the sale of the mine to William Elmore.

So the legend is not all that it is cracked up to be, but what does remain true is that the Elmores were the first to combine the right oil with workable equipment; it is for the operation of a successful plant that the Elmores should be remembered.

2. The Bulk Oil Process

In 1898 the Elmores patented the bulk oil process. Experiments had established that both the oil–water separation and the selective wetting of ore particles by the oil was improved in an acidic environment; thus sulphuric acid became a component in the process. They had also found that a heavy mineral oil was the optimum, being both less dense than water and viscous enough to carry a large ore particle loading in suspension.

Ore ground to a pulp in water was fed with acid and atmospheric residue (the bottom product of an oil refinery's primary distillation column) to the first of three horizontal cylinders. Each had a fixed spiral blade inside to induce effective mixing and rotated at about 6 r.p.m. A constant take-off stream was fed to a vertical stilling vessel, where the oil and water separated, the oil floating. Ore-bearing oil was drawn off as overspill from the top of the vessel. From the bottom, the watery fraction, the gangue and so far unwetted ore, was fed to the second cylinder. More acid and oil were added, and the take-off stream fed to a second stilling vessel. Again the overspill of oil and ore was taken, and the bottom fraction was passed to the third cylinder, where the process was repeated.

The three overspill fractions of oil and ore were blended, heated, and fed to a centrifuge. This resembles a big spin drier, mounted on a vertical axis, with a solid wall and an open top, apart from an inwardly projecting flange all the way round. When spun the contents are thrown to the wall. In operation it was partially filled with water and set spinning at about 1,000 r.p.m. The heated oil and ore was fed to the base of the spinning vessel, thrown to the edge and 'climbed' the wall of water already there. The ore particles were thrown into the water by the centrifugal force and were thus separated from the oil. The oil passed up the centrifuge and was discharged over the inward projecting flange to be recycled for further use. From time to time the centrifuge was emptied of ore which was passed to a second centrifuge for drying.

This was the way Glasdir operated. In a trial 5,000 tons of ore, with 1.5 per cent copper, was treated to recover 80 per cent of the metal in a 10 per cent concentrate, at a cost of less than 5 shillings and 8 pence (28p) per ton. The success lay in the use of atmospheric residue and industrial centrifuges. The Elmores extended operations to a second north Wales mine at Sygun near Beddgelert. An unsuccessful mine, the Elmores bought a controlling share in 1897 and in 1899 they installed their second flotation plant; again it was a technical success. In December 1900 a company called the British Ore Concentration Syndicate began to commercially exploit the process. Further plants were sold to Clogau Gold Mine, between Barmouth and Dolgellau in north Wales, and to Tywarnhayle Mine, in Cornwall, north of Redruth, where Stanley Elmore became a share holder.

Of all these plants, Glasdir was the most successful, although it closed down in 1903. That at Clogau never really operated, being fed with ore of such low grade that one wonders why the expense of a flotation plant was ever contemplated. Sygun's plant was dismantled in 1907, but seems to have worked little after 1903. Tywarnhayle closed its operation in 1904. The fact of the matter was, at every site the process proved to be technically successful, but economically a disaster.

3. The Vacuum Process

The drawbacks of the bulk oil process lay in low efficiencies of contacting pulp and oil, and of disengaging ore and oil, and then in the need to use rotating machinery and the power to rotate it, to achieve both contacting and disengaging. The answer to the problems lay in the Bavarian application of 1877, and… bubbles. It was realized that forced agitation by bubbles of the oil–pulp mix would achieve four ends, namely:

- More efficient oil–ore contacting.
- Elimination of the rotating contactor.
- Effective disengagement by the carry-over of ore particles in the froth of bubbles at the surface of the liquid.
- The elimination of the primary centrifuge.

Thus attempts were made in the early 1900s to create bubbles.

The Elmores' approach was to use the air dissolved in the water of the pulp to create the froth, by pulling a vacuum over the pulp–oil mix. This was aided in carbonate gangues by the generation of carbon dioxide in the acidic environment of the operation. The plant produced was much simpler, with fewer moving parts, and no expensive centrifuge. It was found also that the quantity of oil needed could be reduced. Frank Elmore patented the vacuum process in 1904. In 1905 the British Ore Concentration Syndicate gave way to the Ore Concentration (1905) Company Limited with the Elmore brothers at the helm.

In the vacuum process the thickened pulp, oil and acid were fed to a single horizontal cylindrical mixer equipped with a simple paddle agitator, and a constant feed passed to a small conical pressure vessel. Here a vacuum was maintained and the contents slowly raked. The bubble froth created carried the oil-wetted ore particles up from the liquid surface to spill over

into a collecting vessel. No centrifuging was needed. The process was simple, efficient and a much lower consumer of power.

The earliest vacuum plant appears to have been installed at Falmouth Consols Mine, between Penryn and Truro in Cornwall in 1905, and operated until 1914. Another Cornish installation followed in 1906 at Clitters United Mines, near Gunnislake in east Cornwall, but probably only worked until 1908. It was in 1907 that the process really 'took off'. The company claimed that by May, 70 installations were in use or under construction across the world. These included the further plant at Tywarnhayle, and units at Dolcoath near Camborne in west Cornwall, at Ramsley Mine east of Okehampton on the northern edge of Dartmoor and at Hafna in the Conwy valley in north Wales. In the same year a vacuum plant was installed at Glasdir, still owned by William Elmore's consortium. Output had been down since 1900, perhaps due to the commercial failure of the bulk oil process, but the output rose again in 1907, to remain high until closure in 1914.

The vacuum process was a success, both technically and commercially, for although the British examples all had short lives, this was due to the decline of the mining industry. Indeed, it was probably effective in sustaining British mining longer than gravity methods would have allowed. The process continued in use for coal flotation long after it was superseded in mineral applications by the blown air processes.

4. The Blown Air Process

Across the world the advantages of flotation were rapidly grasped, and many attempts were made both to improve it, and to avoid the Elmore patents. The obvious method to obtain a froth was to actually introduce air bubbles. This was the method followed in 1909 patents by Minerals Separation Ltd and T. J. Hoover, using sub-aeration (i.e., blown air from below).

The first blown air flotation plant in Britain was the eight-cell unit installed by Minerals Separation at the Bonsor Mill of the Coniston Copper Mines in 1912. The operation closed down in 1915. During or soon after the First World War a sub-aeration plant was installed at Gwaithgoch, inland from Aberystwyth, with Government money, to re-treat the dumps of the Frongoch Lead Mine to the north. After an intermittent life it finally closed in the late 1920s. A little concentration of flotation plants arose among the relatively poor mines of the Conwy Valley. Hafna, already been mentioned, used the vacuum process. Soon after 1917 a blown-air unit was installed at Aberllyn Mine, although considerable problems were experienced with froth disengagement. The plant was out of service by the time the mine ceased in 1921. Later ventures in the 1950s at Parc and Trecastle mines both used blown-air units. In 1922 Mill Close Mine, three miles north west of Matlock in the Peak District installed a sub-aeration unit, which although successful, ceased when the mine closed in 1939. At Greenside Mine, above Glenridding at the head of Ullswater, a new plant was installed in 1936. Although it was a blown air plant, it may not have been a sub-aeration type, as it was reported as a new design and not successful. A final pre-Second World War installation might be noted at the Roman gold mine at Ogofau (or Dolau Cothi), twelve miles south east of Lampeter in south west Wales, where the unit, installed too late to save the mine, only proved what success might have been achieved had it been there from the first. The mill only worked for nine months. Its foundations exist at the top of the site, now owned by the National Trust and open to the public as the Dolaucothi Gold Mines.

Overseas the process was adopted with alacrity. The great Rio Tinto mines in south west Spain installed flotation units to recover decomposed pyrites during the First World War, and commissioned a new installation between 1929–31. In 1929 Rio Tinto became the largest shareholder in Minerals Separation Ltd. Elsewhere, extensive development work had taken place in Australia, at Broken Hill Proprietary Company Ltd, from the first introduction of blown air processes. Improvements prior to the First World War enabled previously untreatable dumps rich in zinc to be treated by flotation to recover most of the zinc content. This not only ensured Britain's supply of zinc during the First World War, but also brought the end of British zinc mining.

The Australians also developed selective (or differential) flotation in 1922, using other chemicals than oil to enable different minerals to be selectively extracted from the same pulp. At the same time the idea of selectively wetting the gangue rather than the ore was developed. These ideas were exploited first in the UK by an Australian company from Broken Hill. Sulphide Corporation (later owned by Rio Tinto) bought the Nantymwyn Mine north of Llandovery in south Wales in 1925. Here in a flotation plant worked from 1930, selective conditioning enabled first the separation of lead and then in a second set of cells, zinc. The plant only worked for a few months due to the depression. A similar unit was installed by a South African company at the Parc Mine in the Conwy Valley. Opened in 1952, the installation was successful and ran to 1958 when the mine closed.

To meet this development various types of air-blown flotation cells were developed and patented, of increasing complexity. These included mechanically agitated types, the air being introduced with the impeller, improved sub-aerated types and pneumatically agitated types, and columnar designs exhibiting counter-current flow of the slurry and the bubbles. The various types will not be described: it is an ongoing science.

The two fathers of flotation died in the midst of a developing technology, both at Boxmoor in Hertfordshire, Francis Edward Elmore on 26th July 1932 and Alexander Stanley on 4th March 1944.

Since the Second World War the major mining operations in the British Isles have all used differential flotation to extract every saleable mineral species in the pulp. In modern applications the process is used alongside improved gravity separation methods. There have been or are plants operating in such places as: on the Isle of Man in the 1950s to re-treat the tips of Snaefell Mine (lead and fluorspar); the Peak District (the Cavendish Mill, near Eyam, primarily for fluorspar); in the Lake District, Carrock Fell Mine near Penrith (for tungsten) and Force Crag near Keswick (barytes and zinc); in Weardale at the Broadwood plant and at Ireshopeburn; Cornish mines at Geevor near St Just, South Crofty between Camborne and Redruth, and Wheal Jane between Penryn and Truro (for

several mineral species); the modern copper, lead and zinc mines of Ireland.

5. Industrial Archaeology
The industrial archaeology of flotation is not one of massive remains. All you will find of sites abandoned before the Second War are ruins of mills and foundations, although several sites are most impressive, notably Hafna and Gwaithgoch.

5.1 Bulk Oil
The site at Glasdir (SH 743 223, 1:50,000 sheet 124) is overgrown and inaccessible. Sygun near Beddgelert in Snowdonia (SH 604 488, sheet 115) is open as a tourist attraction. The terraces on which the plant was built stand with some foundations; a site worth a visit. Of the short-lived plant installed at Clogau Gold Mine (in the mill at SH 668 192, sheet 124) next to nothing remains. The site at Tywarnhayle in Cornwall (SW 702 472, sheet 203), has foundations on the hillside, but these are probably from the vacuum unit.

5.2 Vacuum
The best remains of a vacuum plant are at Hafna Mill in the Conwy Valley (SH 781 602, sheet 115), another terraced site, with considerable remains other than the flotation unit; only foundations survive. The foundations at Tywarnhayle (see above) are also probably those of a vacuum plant. As far as I am aware, there are no other vacuum plant remains in Britain.

5.3 Blown Air
Few blown air sites are available. At the Bonsor Mill in the Coniston Mines (SD 290 986, sheet 96) the remains of the mill building and the Pelton turbine that powered the plant are in place. At Gwaithgoch (SN 710 721, sheet 135) the ruins of the mill still stand, terraced above the river Ystwyth, but access is not possible; the site can be viewed from across the river. The Aberllyn site (SH 796 577, sheet 115) is densely overgrown with trees. Hard-to-interpret foundations exist at the short-lived plant at Ogofau (or Dolau Cothi, Dolaucothi Gold Mines, SN 664 400, sheet 146). No other traces of early blown air plants survive.

5.4 Selective operation
This is ongoing technology. There is nothing left at the Parc Mine (SH 787 602, sheet 115) in the Conwy Valley, and at Nantymwyn (SN 787 445, sheet 146) there is no public access to the site. Photographs only show foundations left in 1968.

Bibliography
ANNELS A E, & BURNHAM B C (eds) *The Dolaucothi Gold Mines* (Mineral Exploitation Department, University College, Cardiff; Department of Geography, St David's University College, Lampeter & The National Trust for Wales; 1983, 1986)

AVERY D, *Not on Queen Victoria's Birthday – the story of the Rio Tinto mines* (Collins, London, 1974).

BAWDEN T A. *et al, Industrial Archaeology of the Isle of Man* (David and Charles, Newton Abbot, 1972).

BENNETT J, & VERNON R W. *Mines of the Gwydyr Forest; Part 2, The Hafna Mine, Llanrwst; Part 3, Parc Mine, Llanrwst; Part 4, Aberllyn Mine, Bettws-y-Coed; Part 7, Llanrwst, Coed Gwydyr* (Gwydyr Mines Publications, Cuddington, 1990).

BICK D E, *The Old Metal Mines of Mid-Wales Part 1 Cardiganshire – South of Devil's Bridge* (Pound House, Newent, 1974).

ibid, The Old Copper Mines of Snowdonia (Pound House, Newent, 1982).

ibid, A History of Sygun (Sygun Copper Mine, Beddgelert, 1987).

CULLIMORE S P J, 'The early history of flotation'. *The Trevithick Society Newsletter* No 27, (November 1979), 4–7, with additions & corrections in Newsletters 28, p 12f, 29, p 11, 31, p 11.

Encyclopaedia Britannica, articles; 'Elmore', 'Flotation', 'Metal Mining'.

FORD T D, & RIEUWERTS J H. *Lead Mining in the Peak District* (Peak Park Planning Board, Bakewell, 1968).

HALL G W. *Metal Mines of Southern Wales,* 2nd ed. (Griffin, Kington, 1993)

ibid. The Gold Mines of Merioneth, 2nd Edition, (Griffin, Kington, 1989).

JENKINS P R. *The Glasdir Experiment* (Dragonwheel, Sandcott, 1987).

PERRY J H. *Chemical Engineers' Handbook,* 4th Edition, (McGraw-Hill, New York, 1963).

PICKIN G. 'Visit to Broadwood'. *Friends of Killhope Newsletter* No. 8, (May 1987), 6–10.

RICHARDSON J B. *Metal Mining* (Allen Lane, London, 1974).

SHAW W T. *Mining in the Lake Counties* (Dalesman, Clapham, 1970).

STEPHENS P. 'Wheal Jane'. *The Trevithick Society Newsletter* No. 30, (August 1980), 2–4.

Harwood Lead Mine, Harwood, Teesdale

N A Chapman

This extensive sett is situated in the valley of Harwood in Teesdale and is crossed by a number of east to west bearing veins, besides several north to south cross veins. Reports in the *Mining Journal* on which this article is based indicate that the Harwood Company's operations had been confined to two east–west veins and two cross veins at Scarhead. Also they had driven a level in the Scar Limestone with the intention of intercepting a number of east–west bearing veins to the north of those being worked.

Operations in March of 1859 had produced 25 tons of ore and employed six men. The 'Old Man' had obtained large quantities of ore from workings to the east of the Harwood Company's mines by working the Top Sill. It was believed that the Scar Limestone was unworked and would provide the best returns for the company. To the south–east of the existing workings were a number of veins formerly productive in the Top Sill which would be worth a trial.

They had driven a level 4 fathoms to the No. 1 Cross Vein and found some ore but not enough to be worth dressing. The No. 2 Cross Vein had been reached by a level after driving 13 fathoms and they had continued for a further 21 fathoms. A level underneath the limestone had been driven in a north–easterly direction for 22 fathoms and was expected to cut the Rough Rigg Vein before long.

A call of 6*d*. per share was made with a rebate of 5 per cent if paid in fourteen days. The committee of management was elected consisting of Messrs. Essex, Hardy, White, Robinson, and Crick at a salary of two and a half guineas per month while John Race had been appointed as Mine Manager. Early in 1859 he reported the cutting of a lode in the level, but with no ore in it. Better ore was being cut in the No. 2 Vein, both in the rise being driven and at the ends. It was hoped that they were now clear of the strings in the No. 1 Cross Vein and they intended to drive a rise to locate the limestone. Working in the No. 1 Cross Cut had revealed the cheek of the limestone, but the vein had suddenly moved to the east before rising causing some extra driving to be done. William Vipond, a mining engineer, had been over the mine on February 25th and submitted a report that he approved of operations. He was happy with them driving forwards but suggested the laying of a tram road to ease the long-distance transport. At the time a barrow was used to wheel out the deads.

A meeting of shareholders was held early in March 1859 with C. R. Essex in the chair. Since the last meeting they had sold lead ore amounting to £55. 2*s*. 10*d*. and they had called in £148 making £203. 2*s*. 10*d*. available. Over the period £202. 2*s*. 0*d*. had been spent on the mine and wages leaving £1. 0*s*. 10*d*. However they still owed £111. 8*s*. 11*d* and arrears of calls amounted to £43.

At the setting day towards the end of March, the No. 1 Drift was let to four men at 33*s*. per fathom. Rails had been laid for the waggon in the drift and work was moving faster. This job was let to two men at 50*s*. per fathom. Meanwhile John Race

and a boy were working No. 1 Rough Rigg Vein and producing enough ore to cover the costs. Later in April a rise was being driven in the No. 2 Vein and producing good ore so the decision was taken to stope the area. Enough space was believed to be available to create several floors. The No. 1 Vein was now worth 6 cwt per fathom. Early in May the level cut a string of ore with a throw of 6 inches upwards to the north. Unfortunately the ore was too poor to be worth working. The No. 1 Vein was also described as poor. The end of the No. 2 Vein was turning to the south and they had lost the side wall at the time. Later in the month they were still driving south on No. 2 Vein but had still failed to find the side wall. The driving in the vein was let to two men at 33*s*. per fathom. The No. 1 Vein was somewhat better being let at 36*s*. to two men. Driving the level was let to two men at 54*s*. per fathom. On the surface recent fine weather had permitted dressing operations with about one ton dressed and ready for sale. Further quantities of ore were awaiting dressing while it was hoped to have more ready for sale in two or three days.

Operations on the No. 2 Vein were still concerned with finding the south wall with no success. No. 1 Vein was still poor but returning a little ore. The level was driving without anything worth noting. Three tons of ore were available for sale by the beginning of June but it took a further week to arrange a visit by the Duty Agent to have the ore weighed. Excitement was generated during mid-June when the No. 2 Vein cut a bunch of good ore spangled with iron, it was reported to be worth one ton per fathom. Two men had broken about four tons in a week worth about £14 per ton. The increased output created work for another boy on the dressing floor and he was soon employed.

Early in July William Vipond visited the mine again and provided a short report. The No. 2 Vein had cut a fine bunch of ore from which 4 to 5 tons had been broken. The forefield was driving east at 16 cwt per fathom, while the west end was producing 1 ton per fathom and the work into the roof a similar amount. He believed that the mine would produce 3 tons per week from the four men. Upwards of 2 tons were dressed and ready for sale while a further 3 tons of bouse were on the surface. Eventually 5 tons were sold to W. J. Cookson & Co. for £13. 16*s*. 0*d*. per ton delivered to Alston station less a discount of 1*s*. 4*d*.

It was reported during July that the rich vein of lead cut was improving, it was now 6 fathoms wide but activities were held up by the poor ventilation. The remedy of driving a cross cut to cure the problem was in hand. In the meantime two men were getting the ore. To assist this work access ladders were fitted into a shaft on the vein. Five tons were expected to be ready for sale in a day or two. By the end of the month 6 tons of ore were weighed, 5 for sale and 1 for the royalty dues. Over the summer work progressed slowly because the miners went to gather the hay and later the harvest. Output was still very slow with only a further 6 tons of ore ready for market by the end of September. November was to see severe frosts and snow

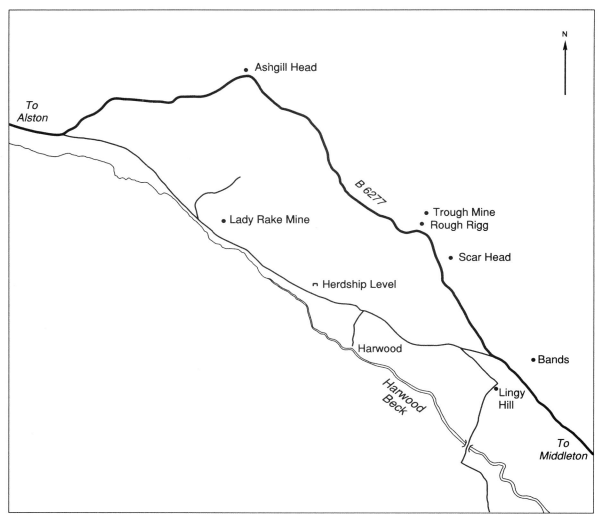

Sketch map of Harwood Lead Mines, Teesdale.

holding up operations. They managed by the beginning of December to have 5 tons 14 cwt ready for sale but the bad weather was preventing dressing activities. Later in the month a report mentioned that the No. 2 Vein continued to hold good with no indications of having been previously worked. In to the New Year of 1860 the vein was better to work and worth 10 cwt per fathom.

On March 10th 1860 the General Meeting was held in Newcastle upon Tyne with James Coxon in the chair. It was disclosed that the costs were £40 in the red and debts of £19 existed. The secretary, Mr Lavington resigned and J. H. Robinson was given a vote of thanks for efficient and free services as Purser for 16 months. He then became Secretary as well. The Agent reported 10 tons of lead ore dressed and about a further 40 tons underground. Unfortunately the prevailing frosty weather was holding up the dressing. A call of 6d. per share was made to clear the debts.

While 40 tons of ore were supposed to be underground it took until the beginning of June to get 8 tons 10 cwt dressed and hauled by carrier to Alston station. Later in the month a further 4 tons 5 cwt were sold for £12. 7s. 6d. per ton. The company commenced the sinking of a shaft at Dry Gill during this period and were soon reporting stones of lead of one to two pounds weight. Cutting south from the shaft they had found lead ore

and were soon busy dressing for the market. On the north to south vein they had cut into old workings proving that the 'Old Man' had known and worked the veins in the past. But the Dry Gill shaft was producing ore from a four feet wide vein of fluorspar mixed with lead and was believed to be the best prospect at the mine. Rails were soon put into the level to take the ore to the dressing floors as it was easier than winding in the shaft.

When during November 1860 a General Meeting was held of the shareholders, a debit balance of £13. 4s. 0d. existed. Liabilities over assets were £10. 11s. 0d. including the value of the plant at the mine. Captain Joseph Race presented a favourable report and probably aided by an excellent meal the meeting broke up on a good note. What can be said is that operations at Harwood continued. Dry Gill continued to produce 10 to 12 cwt of lead ore per fathom and the cross vein east to west was also producing ore. Later in the spring two veins were discovered in the stream at Rough Rigg Syke, to the south of which large quantities of ore had been mined over the years. Of greater interest was the northern section which was unworked.

The level at Scarhead had been neglected for some time and needed putting in order, once this was achieved, driving on a cross cut was commenced. These activities soon resulted in a

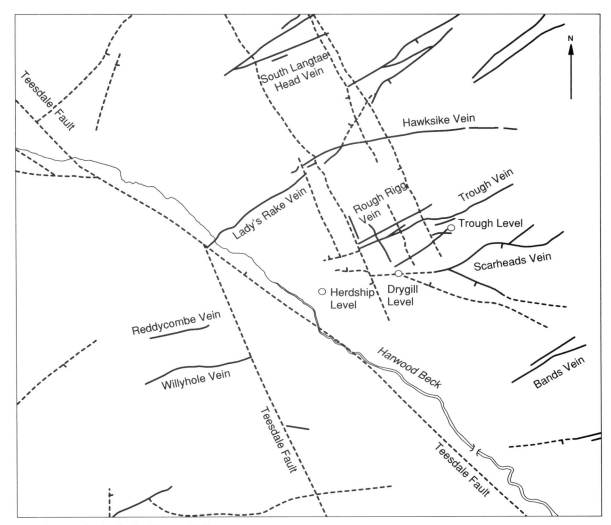

Sketch map of veins in the Harwood Mine area

further 5 tons of dressed ore ready for market. Into 1862 the steady driving of levels and stopes continued with small amounts of lead ore being produced. Typical were the 7 tons 2 cwt sold to the London Lead Company in August at £11. 17s. 6d. per ton at the mine.

To improve operations an example of a 'Puff'[1] appeared in the Mining Journal in November 1861, the mine was noted to be midway between Alston and Middleton-in-Teesdale. The sett was comparatively unexplored, but had yielded large quantities of lead ore from shallow shafts in the past. In a recently discovered vein lead ore was being raised at 4 tons to the fathom in the drift. Both roof and sole were said to be of similar value, in what was noted as one of several veins to be cut. Lead ore was at the time won from the drift east of No. 1 Vein and from a stope in the back of the drift. Working of flats on the side of the vein would yield one ton per fathom. On the surface 9 tons had been dressed and a further 5 were awaiting dressing.

At the General Meeting in Newcastle a cash balance of £54. 11s. 1d. was reported while the mine was still producing 4 tons per fathom from the drift. Fourteen tons were said to be ready for sale. To ease the underground transport a tramway

1. 'Puff' usually a short article or report in the Mining Journal or a newspaper, normally overstating or 'puffing up' the prospects of a mine in order to encourage investment in the company.

was to be put down and the operation was expected to take a month complete. It was decided to apportion the forfeit shares held by the company to the existing shareholders and to open a bank account for the sales receipts. Following the re-election of the directors and a vote of thanks for the Chairman the meeting broke up highly pleased with operations.

During December a further rich vein of lead ore was cut and a shed had to be built at the mine to accommodate the output. Towards the end of the month 26 tons 13 cwt of ore had been sold for £336. 9s. 1d. while 100 to 150 tons were said to be laid in the mine. Over the winter operations continued as possible, but in effect little seems to have been done until the snow was cleared early in February 1862, when the first priority was dressing and despatching the rest of the ore sold in December. By the end of February 12 tons were sold off the mine with another 8 tons on the dressing floors.

Underground the No. 3 cross cut was close to cutting into the new 20 fathom level and following the intersection, it was intended to rapidly drive 10 fathoms to the next cross vein. This had been worked to the south and proved productive, but was still unworked to the north. Driving produced further evidence of the improving richness of the vein and 6 tons of ore.

This encouraged shareholders to visit the mine over the May Bank Holiday, when in lovely weather, they inspected the surface and underground and following the usual refreshments, went away pleased with the outing. The Mining Journal published a short article on the event and went on to mention 25 tons of ore ready for market. The property was described as an amalgamation of six setts of two miles extent east to west and about one and half miles wide. Because of the recent increase in output the company were proposing to erect a crushing mill. It would appear that basic hand cobbing or bucking methods of dressing had sufficed to this date.

At the General Meeting in July 1863, William Vipond and John Race gave a long report on operations at the mine since the previous November. The No. 1 Vein had been driven east for 18 fathoms and stoped for 19 fathoms at the No. 2 cross cut to intercept the vein. A point of interest was that ore was found only in the Middle Limestone, both Top and Bottom Limestone were found to be poor.

During January 1864 the decision had been taken to drive the No. 2 cross cut to cut the vein to the east and during this operation a rich vein was found. Workings were being developed both east and west in this vein at the time of the General Meeting in February. John Race was able to give an optimistic report on the mine for the shareholders. For the future, a north–south vein was known to be only a few fathoms away and was expected to be intercepted shortly. Over the period under review 72 tons 17 cwt of lead ore had been produced and 7 tons were on the dressing floors. He went on to comment that a large portion of the sett was totally unworked with a number of productive veins known to cross the area, so with reduced dues and greater investment, he believed the unworked area could yield greater profits.

At the General Meeting held on November 28th 1863, Joseph Race gave a report on progress since August. They had driven 15 fathoms from the No. 3 cross cut in the vein at that time, since a further 14 fathoms 3 feet had been driven making a grand total of 29 fathoms 3 feet of progress. Part of the drift had been stoped for 11 fathoms and a rise had been put up 3 fathoms from the end of the drift in the vein. Also since August they had stoped 12 fathoms of ore ground in the west end and raised nearly 20 tons of ore. The level had been driven 12 fathoms to the east but had not yet cut the cross vein. Work continued at the mine into December with operations centring on an old shaft sunk to the south side of their vein to work another east–west vein. They cleared out the debris and followed the 'Old Man's' Drift north on top of the limestone and through the present vein without sinking into it. The 'Old Man' had worked two parallel east–west veins further to the north. Further investigation revealed the existence of two complete veins tried but not worked running probably the full length of the Harwood Drift. This was considered to be an important discovery with a large area of veins to be prospected. In the first instance this shaft was improved to supply fresh air to the level and was laddered as an access to the workings.

Into 1864, operations continued on the drift with a cross string cut and work in the Trough Low Level commenced. On the surface a severe winter of frost and snow prevented dressing and most other activities. Fortunately 20 tons of lead ore were got away to market just before the weather broke. By March the weather had improved to the extent that no further problems

were expected, so the dressing plant was kept busy. Four tons had been processed and a further 4 tons were on the floors awaiting dressing. At the time most of the ore was coming from the Trough Level. A month later the dressed ore had risen to 12 tons and great things were expected from the nearly completed Trough Level. By September ore was being raised from the No. 1 east stope, while in the Trough Level a highly mineralised string had been cut. From these sources, 10 tons of ore were sold to Messrs. Shield and Dinning in October.

Towards the end of the following month a north–south vein was cut which they believed was the Drygill Cross Vein. At the same period a vein was cut in the Trough Low Level and claimed to be the Trough Vein. Operations early in 1866 consisted of working a vein at Scar Head, driving a cross cut from the level west and working on the forefield of the drift east. At the Trough Level they were getting good stones of lead during driving on a cross vein and from this, they expected to cut an east–west vein shortly. In the Trough Vein, the working were to east and west, worth 8 cwt per fathom. The company had sold 94 tons 10 cwt of lead concentrates from the mine during 1865 and boasted of a further 20 tons ready to be dressed.

Work had commenced on a new cross cut to the north called Locke's Level, this was expected to intercept, after driving a few fathoms, a new vein noted on the surface. In expectation of cutting a rich vein a new water course was being cut to power a water wheel at the entrance to the level and a dressing floor area was levelled. The main source of lead ore at the period was from stopes above a drift in the limestone. This was reported to be worth 3 tons of ore per fathom worked. John Race was able to offer 60 tons of ore for sale during May, most of which had been won from this vein. Rich ore was still coming from the mine in August and 24 tons were ready to be weighed.

Later in the month it was reported that over 100 tons had been raised in twelve months by six men working one vein at shallow depth. In a few weeks a new level would enable extraction to be done cheaper and hopefully open new veins. According to Mr Evan Hopkins a well-known civil engineer, 'The Harwood sett was the best undeveloped mineral property in the North of England'. Naturally, this quote was widely circulated in the mining press. A report for the middle of September mentioned about 15 tons of lead ore broken and partly dressed on the floors. By the middle of October this figure had risen to 24 tons and work was continuing on the dressing floors being constructed at the mouth of Locke's Level. It was hoped that before the end of November this heading would be equipped with rails and worked as a horse level.

In fact this objective was achieved, with Locke's Level operating from the beginning of December with horse haulage. This improvement helped to boost the output with 29 tons 4 cwt of lead concentrates being sold off the mine late the same month. Early in 1868 the workings at Scar Head were reported to be poor, while operations centred on pushing Trough Level up to the Mouncer Cross Vein in the hope of finding ore. It was planned to enter the Trough Vein from the level and improve the haulage in this way. Output appears to have been slow to develop with only 6 to 7 tons of ore broken on the floors by the end of April. On the bright side the deep level had cut a vein of dark mineral fluorspar and lead ore, worth about one ton per fathom and easy to work.

Most of the output to date had come from the workings at Scar Head but now the veins were poor and the veins at Trough and Locke's Level were beginning to produce lead ore. Also a new vein called Richardson's was producing ore. With a reduction in the royalty dues, it was hoped that a new period of profits and more important, dividends was forecast. Operations to improve the access to Trough Vein were completed by June and the mine horses were employed leading ore from this vein. It was stated to be worth one ton of ore per fathom at this period. Twelve tons of concentrates were soon available for sale on the mine.

Driving at the Scar Head workings located a new cross vein in the southern part of the sett. Trenching on the surface was resorted to, sinking down twelve feet in clay, ore and spar. Meanwhile, at Trough Head, in the level driving east, they had cut a small flat with ore in it. Work on the Low Level had also cut a vein which was believed to be Richardson's though this was not certain. Irrespective of names, little was produced from the workings until near Christmas when 24 tons of concentrates were sold.

The mine remained poor into the new year, the only ore being produced from driving on a branch of the Trough Vein and a stope being developed at the intersection. Because of the frosts and snow it was into April before they could start dressing the ore. It took until the end of June to get the ore dressed and it amounted to 10 tons plus 2 tons more as royalty dues. Messrs. Walton of the Bollihope smelter sent their carrier to collect. During October operations centred on the Mouncer Cross Vein, which was very hard to cut and set to six men. The vein was confused and believed to be divided into two or three sections. Work continued on the vein into 1870. Early in the New Year, they cut a string of clay rider about 6 inches wide with some stones of ore about the size of a hen's egg. By the end of March the drift was believed to be near the Trough Vein as the strata were displaced upwards.

Nothing further is reported until June when the level was stated to have more lead ore in it. Late in August it was believed that a new vein had been discovered while sinking in Harwood Spa. It would appear they had moved to a new location and commenced sinking a shaft. This was 2 fathoms 2 feet deep in clay mixed with spar and sulphur, fostering the belief that a vein was near. Heavy rain later in the year brought operations in the shaft to a halt while driving in Locke's Level was producing 8 cwt per fathom and richer ore was expected. Unfortunately operations at the Spa sinking were held up over the winter and into early 1871. Once the snows melted in the new year hopes were entertained of getting busy at the sinking but hiring the men took longer than expected.

At this point there is a gap in the reports until December 1875 when a William Tallentire continued the series. At the time they were driving a rise to the top of the limestone at the Herdship Level and had small pieces of lead ore throughout the rise. He believed that the vein could be worked at a profit at a later stage. Activities continued with the driving of the Herdship Level into 1876. A drive to the north was commenced along the

vein which was reported as 2 feet wide at the bottom of the limestone. This vein was later reported as being worth 8 cwt of lead ore per fathom. Operations centred on pushing the main level forwards to cut a number of north to south veins with good prospects of finding workable deposits of lead ore.

On the surface operations had begun on the construction of a bridge over the beck to provide access to a large area ideal for the construction of dressing floors. These were designed to handle the output from the Herdship Level, to which a tram road was laid. Driving on the Herdship Level was progressing well with lead being won from the north and south end workings. During the summer the level cut an east to west vein, producing ore fit to be dressed on the floors. This produced 2 tons 8 cwt of saleable concentrates. Operations were centred on a rise in the No. 1 Cross Vein to prove its worth in the limestone and to intercept a north–south vein believed to be near. This vein had formerly been productive at the Scar Head Mines and hopes were entertained of riches here. At the time ore was being produced from the north and south ends of the No. 2 Cross Vein. Herdship Level was driven east gradually into the new year with little alteration from the rest of the workings.

During early June 1877 the level cut a further north to south vein with solid pieces of lead ore reported. The miners had driven the level east 4 fathoms in the month. Operations centred on driving south in the vein with good samples of ore being produced. The Herdship Level was now driven north on the same vein, producing ore worth one and a half bings per fathom. Stoping in September was being undertaken on a vein in the Herdship Level with a red mineral worth 10 cwt per fathom being produced. In the south end about 6 cwt of ore was being produced by stoping. On the surface dressing was being pushed as fast as possible. Later in September floods revealed the existence of an east–west vein about 50 fathoms ahead of the present level. William Tallentire had been dialling the once-productive Dry Gill Vein with a view to reworking.

By the middle of October the mine was able to sell to Dinnings 4 tons of concentrates with a further 1 ton 5 cwt available at the mine. Work continued on the vein at the Herdship Level with stoping being developed at the north end. The vein in the stope was about 5 feet wide and composed of red mineral with pieces of solid ore. Operations on the vein continued into the new year with good progress driving east being reported. The miners were finding large quantities of stones, while the work was worth 8 cwt per fathom. Work continued to produce lead ore in small quantities, while during April 1878, 12 fathoms of driving yielded 1 ton per fathom of lead ore. In the middle of October 1878 the driving of No. 2 North End intercepted an east to west vein, which, when stoped yielded 8 tons of concentrates. They were expecting to cut the Dry Gill Vein in the near future.

At this point the reports end with an air of expectation, which had kept the miners going for years. These mines probably needed to work lead ore worth from 8 cwt per fathom upwards, getting below this break-even figure meant a steady drain on the shareholders pockets. As can be noted above, the percentage was, in later years, seldom above the required limit. With the steady decline in the price of lead ore in the 1870s the mine had little or no chance of paying costs. It then became a case of how long would the shareholders pay up.

In this case the end came somewhere towards the close of 1878 when the miners were paid off and the plant sold to pay debts, while the workings slowly filled with water and remained waiting for better times.

Mineral Statistics (after Robert Hunt)

Year	Lead Ore Produced
1859	17 tons
1860	8 tons
1865	94 tons
1866	137 tons
1876	3 tons
1877	8 tons
1878	16 tons

While the Herdship Level output is noted as:

1877	9 tons
1879	5 tons

References
Mining Journal 1859 to 1878

Hunder Beck – A lost lead mine in Baldersdale, Co. Durham

John Pickin

The Balder is a major tributary of the Tees, joining the river at Cotherstone near Barnard Castle. Although Baldersdale lies within the Northern Pennine Orefield the only references in the geological literature to mining in the dale are for a number of small coal trials exploiting outcrops of the Mirk Fell and Tanhill coals (Burgess and Holiday 1979, 49). These trials are likely to have been worked in the eighteenth and early nineteenth centuries to provide fuel for local farms and limekilns and they belong to an agricultural tradition quite separate from the contemporary lead mining industry. There is some evidence, however, to suggest that lead was also searched for and possibly worked in one remote part of Baldersdale and this is examined below.

History

The earliest reference to metal mining in Baldersdale is in a counterpart lease of 1727 between Ferdinand Huddleston of Millom Castle and William Hutchinson of Barnard Castle (DRO: D/St/B2/11). This was a 21 year lease of all the lead mines in Hunderthwaite, the township on the north side of the dale, and included the right 'to dig Hushes'. Nothing more is known about the success or otherwise of this venture but it is interesting to note that a letter written in 1802 by John Bayles, a local prospector, states 'Hunderthwaite Lordship has never been known to Contain any Vein of Lead or other minerals' (DRO: D/St/B2/43) which suggests that earlier attempts at mining and prospecting in this part of Baldersdale had proved fruitless.

The documentary evidence for mining in Cotherstone township, which forms the southern part of the dale, is slightly more expansive and indicates that there were a number of attempts to prospect lead in the upper reaches of Hunderbeck. This is a desolate section of Cotherstone Moor. It lies at 390 m AOD, is some seven miles from Cotherstone and a mile and a half from Clove Lodge, the nearest farm and road. There is no obvious access to the site and its operation during the eighteenth and nineteenth centuries must have posed serious problems.

The earliest record for operations at Hunderbeck is a 'Take-note for Mining and Hushing for Lead Oar' dated 1 May 1773 (DRO: D/St/B2/36). It was issued by agents for the Duke of Devonshire and John Bourn, co-owners of the joint manor of Cotherstone, to Christopher Rain of Reeth, Henry Temple of West Briscoe, and John Kipling of Blackton and was to be for a period of 11 years with duty payable on 'every Eight Bing or Measure of ore.' Rain may well have had a background in the Swaledale mines but Temple and Kipling were Baldersdale men, probably local tenant farmers with little direct experience of mining . The agreement allowed the three men to:

'… work for Lead or Lead ore in a certain piece of Ground parcel of the Common waste ground lying and being within the Joint Manor of Cotherstone – and commonly called by the name of Hundabeck. And that we [Rain et al] and such other persons as shall join with us in this undertaking shall and will without loss of time Work Drive Sink or Hush for Lead or Lead ore in and through all the said Ground called Hundabeck beginning at a certain place towards the lower end of the said Beck commonly called Crawlah-gill-foot and so up the said Beck to a certain place whence two Millstones now lie and have laid for a great number of years. And within and through Six Hundred yards on each side of the said Beck or Gill from the bottom where the water now runs.'

This was essentially a prospecting agreement to search the area of ground west of Crawlaw Gill (NY 929 168). The restriction of this area to a band 600 yards (300 m) wide either side of Hunder Beck was necessary because Cotherstone township at this point formed a wedge of ground sandwiched between the townships of Hunderthwaite and Lartington to the north and south respectively. These townships belonged to different manor estates and so were subject to separate mineral arrangements. Recent fieldwork has failed to locate the two millstones which marked the western extent of the lease but the area may have extended as far as the watershed on the Westmorland county boundary.

The scale of these 1773 operations is unknown but the outcome is summarised in a pencil note on the outside of the document which states 'Partners Expended £104 in trying sd. Lead Mine, & got no ore materials.'

In January 1808 Joseph Dent entered into an agreement:

'to take a lead Mine known by the name of Hunda Beck in the Manor of Cotherstone in the County of Yorke for Twelve Years for paying one fifth part of all Ore won or raisd at the said Mine to be boundered on the South and East by Crawley Rivulet by the County of Westmorland on the West and Balder Rivulet on North to work the said premises with not less than four men' [D/St/B2/452].

This must be the mine prospected or worked by the partnership in 1773 but nothing is known of the success or otherwise of Dent's venture.

More information on Hunderbeck mine is contained in the Cotherstone Township tithe map of 1838. This shows a series of mining features including a dam, three hushes, a level, a shaft and a shop at the confluence of Coal Gill with Hunder Beck (Fig. 2). These are the only mineral workings marked in the whole of the township and it would seem probable that this the same as the mine mentioned in the agreements of 1773 and 1808. Of particular interest is the depiction on the map of 'old' and 'new' levels and 'old' and 'new' hushes which indicates that mining was in progress at the time of the tithe survey. Further evidence for activity at this time is a take-note issued by the joint manor in 1839 to John Archer Foster of Bishop Auckland who was acting on behalf of Henry Anderson and John Hodgson and partners. This agreement covered all the ground in the upper reaches of Hunder Beck and was for a period of 21 years at ⅕th bing duty (D/St/B2/51).

By 1842 the mineral rights for Cotherstone township had been acquired by the London Lead Company which, through its agent Robert Bainbridge, took a lease on all the lead mines in 'the Several Manors and Townships of Lune, Holwick,

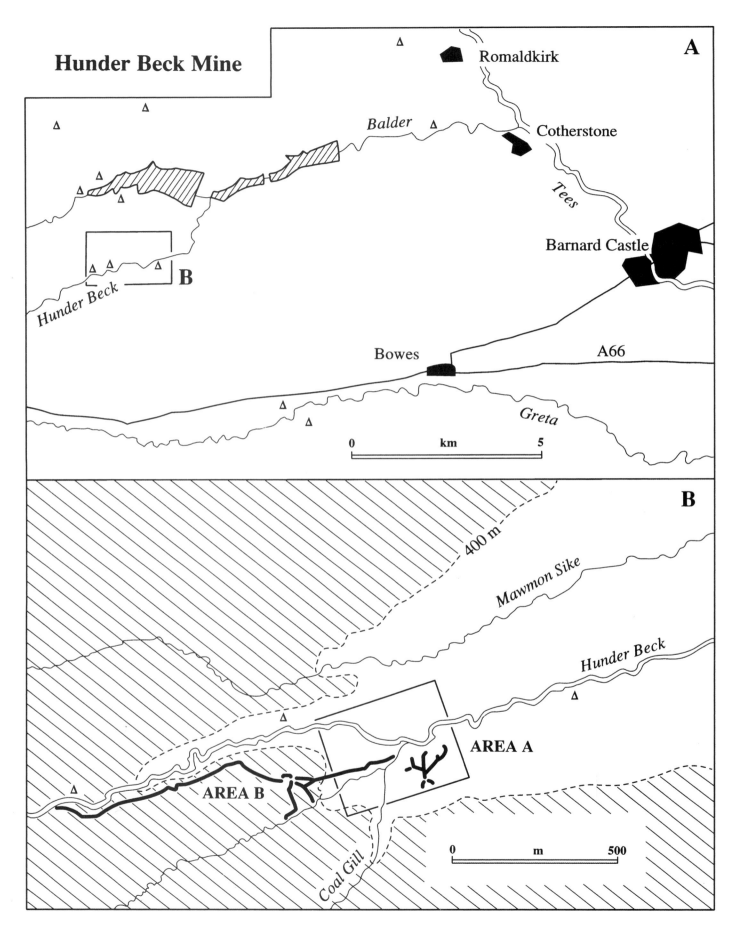

Fig. 1. Location of Hunder Beck Mine; the open triangles are coal mines.

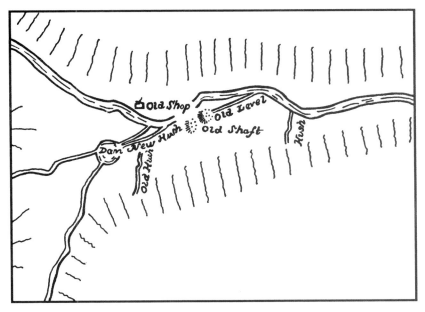

Fig. 2. Hunder Beck Mine as shown on the 1838 Tithe Survey.

Mickleton, Hunderthwaite and Cotherstone.' This lease included 'a power for Hushing by the Lessees in the Waste or uninclosed parts — for the discovery and winning of Mines and Veins' (D/St/B2/59). The Lead Company lease was extended in 1844 for a 31 year period and renewed for a similar period in 1855 (D/St/B2/67). These leases were part of the attempt by the Lead Company to obtain a monopoly in the Teesdale mining field and it is unlikely if any further major work was carried out after this date at Hunder Beck or indeed at any of the other poor prospecting sites on Cotherstone and Romaldkirk moors.

The first edition Ordnance Survey (OS) 6 inch sheet of 1857 does not mark any lead mine on Hunder Beck but it does show a stream running south west from the junction of Hunder Beck and Coal Gill which corresponds to the old hush shown on the 1838 Tithe survey. More importantly, the 1857 map also shows, but does not name, a new hushing complex east of Coal Gill which suggests a major period of prospecting or mining at some time between 1838 and 1857. The same pattern of hush channels is shown, unaltered, on the second edition OS of 1898. This edition also marks, but for the first time, a level driven into the east bank of Coal Gill just above its confluence. It is shown as disused but does suggest further small scale operation in the second half of the nineteenth century.

The Site
The principal workings appear to be on the south side of Hunder Beck immediately below its confluence with Coal Gill (Area A: NY 915 164). The surviving evidence indicates that activity was concentrated on the location and underground exploitation of a small lead vein running WSW–ENE. between Hunder Beck and Dun Moss. The western extent of this vein was also searched for and possibly worked by a large hush or opencut north of Dun Moss Sike (Area B: NY 913 163).

Area A (Fig. 4)
The beck at this point runs through a broad, meandering channel cut into the generally flat moorland on either side. There are no exposures of bedrock in the immediate vicinity

and much of the ground exposed by the beck comprises thick deposits of glacial clays and gravel capped by peat. It is probable that winter floods and land slips in this soft ground have destroyed or masked many parts of the mine although enough surface features survive to provide some idea of the size and methods of the operation.

An 'Old Level' is shown on the 1838 survey. The entrance to this can no longer be located and must be assumed to have run-in long since but a short length of ditch with low banks either side (Fig. 4:1) can be interpreted as the outfall channel between the level's portal and the beck. No spoil heaps survive outside the presumed level entrance but these are likely to have been removed by past flood action, a situation which can be observed at many other North Pennine mines with a portal entrance at stream level. The level would appear to have been driven in a south-westerly direction to connect with the 'Old Shaft' of the 1838 survey and one of two hollows on the edge of the stream bank (Fig. 4:2) must mark the collapsed collar of this shaft with the other probably being a collapse cone on the line of the level.

Some 80 m south of the 'Old Shaft' is a small dam (Fig. 4:3). Its earth-built wall is 2 m wide and the pond behind, which was fed from the adjacent stream, covers an area of 4 m x 12 m. The bank has the gentle curve common to other post-medieval hushing dams in the North Pennines and is broken by a single, off-centre entrance from which two water channels can be traced. One channel runs north-east for 60 m before splitting and curving north to the steep bank edge above Hunder Beck. The other channel runs north for 20 m and then bifurcates with the two new channels both exhibiting a sharp change in direction before cutting steep, short gashes into the bank edge. The western channel incorporates a shallow ditch running back towards the side stream which can best be interpreted as an overflow channel. Aerial photography indicates a further two linear channels on the east bank of Coal Gill which may be part of the same hushing system (Fig. 4:4) but it has to be remembered that there are major problems in this sort of landscape in differentiating between natural stream cuts and man-made water courses. The various water channels fall within the area marked as 'Old Hush' on the 1838 survey.

The 1838 survey marks a dam at the bottom of Coal Gill and shows a 'New Hush' running at stream level from there to the south side of Hunder Beck. A short bank on the west side of Coal Gill (Fig. 4:5) may be the remains of this dam and an embanked channel can be followed for approximately 10 m on the opposite side of the stream. This leads to a disturbed area (Fig. 4:6) where a parcel of ground has been worked parallel to the south bank of Hunder Beck. It takes the form of a steep sided trench with a narrow bottom and a spoil tip along the north edge and would seem to relate to the 'New Hush' of the survey. Immediately north-west of this, and closer to the stream edge, is an eroded length of bank with partial dry stone revetment (Fig. 4:7). It appears to be separate from the nearby

Fig 3. Aerial photograph of Hunder Beck Mine Area A.
Photograph No. TBM AP 1993.1.28 taken by B Vyner as part of The Bowes Museum archaeological survey of Baldersdale, 1993.

hush system and may be the flood-damaged remains of a spoil tip or platform associated with the level shown close to this position on the 1898 OS map. Nothing survives of the level itself.

On the north side of the beck a rectangular dry-stone cabin, 2.5 m x 4 m (Fig. 4:8), has been built on an area of flat ground above the flood level of the stream. It has a sloping roof of massive sandstone slabs resting on a pine roof frame, a single door and unglazed window and contains a small hearth. Outside is a small enclosure surrounded by a dry stone wall. The cabin is still used by shepherds today and is similar to a number of other combined shelters and sheep pens on the more isolated parts of Cotherstone Moor (e.g. Hunder Rigg NY 923 166; Slates Hill NY 929 162). As a simple functional structure it is hard to date but it occupies the same position as the 'Old Shop' shown on the 1838 survey and may well be the same building.

Area B (Fig. 1B)
Area B consists of a hushing complex which explored a westerly continuation of the vein. A leat takes water from Hunder Beck at NY 905 163, over one kilometre upstream from and 40 m higher than the main mine described above. The leat can still be followed as a discontinuous trench for 650 m until it feeds a dam built on the spur between Hunder Beck and Dun Moss Sike. The dam is earth built and the pond behind covers an area of approximately 11 m x 28 m. A second channel enters the dam from the south and appears to be an additional feeder leat taking water from Dun Moss Sike. The dam bank has a single entrance from which two parallel channels run steeply down slope to converge after 200 m. This single channel, which is now an active surface stream, rapidly forms a steep trench which reaches a width of 12 m and a depth of 5 m before terminating at Coal Gill (Fig. 4:9). This is a classic hush gutter but its V-shape profile is probably the result of later erosion which may mask the base of the original excavation.

Other workings
The 1857 OS sheet marks coal levels upstream of Hunder Beck Mine at NY 913 164 and a rock-cut portal is still visible in a small sandstone outcrop at this point. Another level survives some 300 m downstream of the mine, NY 919 165, and is also shown on the 1898 OS sheet. Its absence from the earlier maps suggests that it post-dates the workings at Hunder Beck mine but it is not known whether it was driven for lead or coal. The fine, arched portal is intact and it is possible that underground

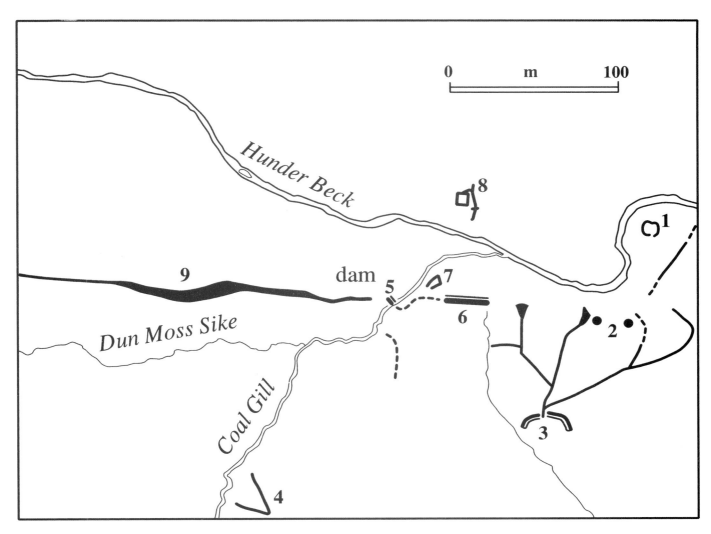

Fig. 4. Transcription of the main features shown on the aerial photograph (Fig. 3).

exploration could provide an answer to the type of mineral being worked.

Discussion

The documentary and field evidence show that Hunder Beck mine was worked on a number of occasions over a 100-year period. At least four phases of operation can be identified.

Phase 1. The earliest episode appears to have been exploratory work concerned with exposing and possibly exploiting the vein close to the Hunder Beck – Coal Gill confluence. This phase relates to the lease taken out by Rain, Temple and Kipling in 1773 and may be the 'Old Workings' shown on the 1838 Tithe survey. The operations comprised a series of narrow channels fed by a single dam which were placed to hush the south bank of the beck, presumably to remove peat and glacial clays in an attempt to expose and prove any vein at this point. Cranstone (1992, 46) categorises this type of hush as a prospecting hush.

The vein was also tested underground by a level and shaft. Elsewhere in the North Pennines underground workings tend to post-date hushing but there is no evidence for this at Hunder Beck and it may be that both underground and surface operations were conducted at the same time.

Phase 2. This phase relates to the 'New' workings shown on the 1838 survey. Activity is still concentrated in the same area as the earlier operations but appears now to incorporate an extension of the existing hushing system combined with a determined attempt to prospect or work the south bank of the beck. The 1838 survey clearly marks a dam at stream level and, as mentioned above, traces of this can still be identified on the ground. The dam is too low for conventional gravity hushing but the associated water channel and 'hushed' trench suggest that some form of hydraulic mining was intended. The most likely explanation is that the dam and water course were designed to remove some of the thick glacial deposits masking the bank of the beck. This operation, especially if carried out in combination with the more conventional hushing processes being undertaken above the bank, would expose the bedrock and help locate the vein. Alternatively this may be what Cranstone (1992, 47) calls a washing hush in which case its primary purpose was to wash dressing floor tailings or, more likely, to re-work the waste heaps resulting from earlier hushing; the size of the trench at the end of the water course and the suggestion of a definite waste tip on its north side support the idea that this operation was to examine and rework hushing spoil. A third suggestion is that the dam and trench were constructed for the deliberate alluvial working of float and shoad ore in the bank's overburden. Raistrick (1965, 11) suggested that there may have been early alluvial mining near Garrigill in the South Tyne but there is little evidence for this process elsewhere in the region. Was alluvial mining never undertaken in the potentially rich stream deposits of the North Pennines or is its apparent absence due more to a combination of site erosion and lack of fieldwork?

Phase 3. This phase comprises the large leat, dam and hush system on Dun Moss shown on the 1857 map and which can still be recognised unaltered on the ground today. The scale of operations undertaken in the first two phases is comparatively small and is typical of the work which could have been achieved, often on a seasonal basis, by a small partnership of farmer-miners. The hushing system of Phase 3 is altogether a much larger and more intensive undertaking, indicating a mining company rather than a low capital partnership. The map evidence shows that the hush system was constructed and used between 1838 and 1857 and it may be no coincidence that the mineral rights for Cotherstone Moor were acquired by the London Lead Company (LL Co.) in 1842. The direct link cannot of course be demonstrated but a case could be made, based on the coincidence between the dates, to suggest that this phase of intensive hushing should be attributed to the LL Co.

Phase 4. The evidence for phase 4 is the collapsed level at the end of Coal Gill which is shown as disused on the 1898 OS map. This may have been driven, possibly by the LL Co. and after the completion of hushing on Dun Moss, to test the extent of the old workings at the original Hunder Beck Mine. Alternatively, it could have been part of a completely separate operation to prospect or work coal and was contemporary with the coal level downstream at NY 919 165. It must be assumed that all work had ceased before, and possibly long before, 1898 and that phase 4 marks the last episode in the history of Hunder Beck Mine.

Hunder Beck Mine is similar to many small ventures in the North Pennines which were encouraged by the mining boom of the late eighteenth century and continued to be worked intermittently into the middle decades of the nineteenth century. What makes Hunder Beck different from these other mines is that it was an attempt to locate and exploit lead in remote and inhospitable countryside on the very edge of the known orefield. How many other 'lost' mines still lie unrecorded in our more desolate upland areas?

Acknowledgements
I would like to thank Ros Nichols, Niall Hammond, Blaise Vyner and the staff of the Durham Record Office. Mrs Nan Hamilton of Cotherstone allowed access to her copy of the Tithe Survey and Mr Purvis of Clove Lodge allowed access to the site which is on private land.

Bibliography
BURGESS, I. C. & HOLLIDAY D. W., Geology of the country around Brough-under-Stainmore, (Mem. Geol. Surv. GB, 1979).

CRANSTONE, D. 'To Hush or not to Hush: when, where and how?', in Men Mines & Minerals of the North Pennines, ed. B Chambers, (Houghton-le-Spring, 1992). pp 41–48

RAISTRICK, A. A History of Lead Mining in the Pennines, (London, 1992).

Some Legal Aspects of Metalliferous Mining Leases in Weardale, Co. Durham, c. 1844

(A Nineteenth Century Conundrum)

W. F. Heyes

Introduction

Lead mining in the Northern Pennines, of which Weardale is a constituent part, has been extensively researched and documented by many workers and much research continues today. In contrast, the subject of iron mining in the same area has been devoted scant attention, probably because the main iron mining era lasted but 50 years (c. 1840 to 1890). Nevertheless, as an integral part of the metalliferous mining industry in the Northern Pennines it is important that this aspect of mining history is not overlooked.

Rights to the mineral riches of Durham were granted to the Bishops of Durham before 1154, for in that year King Stephen issued a charter confirming the grant of the mineral rights in Weardale to Bishop Hugh Puiset. The Bishops were free to work the mines themselves or to lease these to speculators on a royalty basis, claiming 'duty ore'. One of the earliest Weardale mineral leases known dates from 1380, when Bishop Hatfield leased to Alice Birkby, a widow, the Weardale mines for a period of 50 years. Similar leases dated 1391 and 1401 are recorded.[1] The Bishops, it seems, preferred to lease their mining rights for large areas of ground rather than leasing a length of vein which was the commonest practise in the seventeenth and early eighteenth century.[2] Thus in 1696 the Bishop of Durham granted the rights to the Weardale lead ore to Sir William Blackett; the Blackett–Beaumont family continued to hold these rights until the 1880s.

By 1844 separate leases of the mining rights for lead ore, for ironstone and for copper, tin and other minerals had been granted in Weardale. This in itself was not a problem, but when the rights to the various minerals were leased by different parties on (or under) the same piece of ground, matters became somewhat complicated—because the different minerals often occurred intermixed in Northern Pennine veins. At best some working arrangement would be required between the different parties, at worst a protracted legal wrangle might ensue, thereby severely limiting the lessor's income from duty ore until such time that the legal arguments could be resolved. The complexity of the situation in Weardale in 1844 is iillustrated in Fig. 1. The rights to the lead ore, galena, belonged to the Blackett–Beaumont family of Allendale, originally granted by the Bishop of Durham in 1696; this lease also included the small quantity of silver (typically 5–15 oz per ton of lead) that naturally occurred in the galena and was inseparable until the lead ore was smelted. Rights to all other minerals were leased to G. Pearson (one of the Bishop's Agents) of Harperley Hall, eventually passing to George Hutton Wilkinson by virtue of his marriage to Pearson's daughter.[3] The Blackett–Beaumont family themselves operated the mines leased to them by the Bishop and smelted the lead ore in their own mills. Wilkinson, on the other hand, sublet his mineral rights to various parties, but in so doing, further complicated what was already a complex situation, though unrecognised at that time. In an attempt to untangle the legal complexities Wilkinson sought recourse to independent judicial opinion. The presentation of the case is outlined in a document,[4] dated 1844, prepared for submission to a QC. The quotes which follow are extracted from this document.

Rightful Access to Intermixed Minerals

As the mineral veins in Weardale rarely, if ever, consist of a single pure mineral, a mineralised vein will typically be composed of the metal ores galena, zinc blende, iron minerals together with the gangue minerals fluorspar and silica. The Blackett–Beaumont family held the lead ore (galena) rights, Wilkinson the rights to all other minerals. At the time the Blackett–Beaumonts obtained the lease to mine lead ore their aim was indeed just that, i.e. they had no interest whatsoever in any other mineral (except of course the silver which was inseparable from the galena). All other minerals that occurred in the lead veins were considered worthless or existed in uneconomic quantities. Those unwanted minerals that could be separated by hand from the galena during the mining operation were left underground, e.g. limonite, which often occurred on the walls of the vein and thus could be left in situ; minerals admixed with the galena were separated during washing and then discarded as waste, often being washed into the local river system and eventually dispersed by winter floods. In the early 1840s, sometime between 1840 and 1844, it was discovered that the waste discarded as worthless by the Blackett-Beaumonts consisted of extensive quantities of the valuable iron minerals siderite (iron carbonate) and limonite (a hydrated iron oxide).

When Wilkinson became aware that minerals which were rightfully his under his lease from the Bishop were literally being thrown away by the Blackett–Beaumonts during the washing process, his concern was for the legality of this action. The lawful options open to Wilkinson to enable him to obtain access to this newly discovered source of iron ore were pursued by seeking independent legal guidance:

'Questions are now likely to arise between the different parties as to their respective rights and as to how the mines are to be worked or managed so as to secure to each party what they may be entitled to.'

Wilkinson did not question the ownership of the different ores—this was clearly defined in the leases to Beaumont and himself from the Bishop of Durham; Beaumont had not surpassed his legal right, for he had taken from the mines only what was rightfully his, i.e. the lead ore; the other ores he had left behind after separation, either in the mines, on the dumps or in the river as a consequence of the washing operation:

'Mr Beaumont however has hitherto gone on and wasted the minerals he has found in working for lead or left them in the mines.'

Wilkinson could only seek a legal opinion on his own rights in law to gain access to the iron ore to which he was entitled:

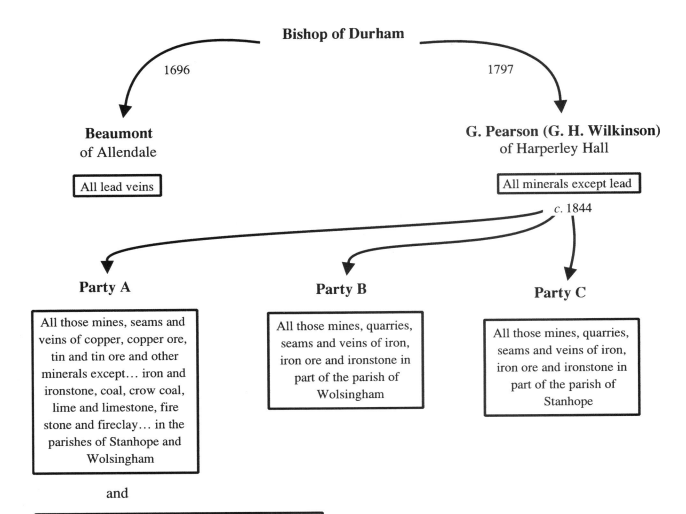

Bishop of Durham

1696

1797

Beaumont
of Allendale

All lead veins

G. Pearson (G. H. Wilkinson)
of Harperley Hall

All minerals except lead

c. 1844

Party A

All those mines, seams and
veins of copper, copper ore,
tin and tin ore and other
minerals except… iron and
ironstone, coal, crow coal,
lime and limestone, fire
stone and fireclay… in the
parishes of Stanhope and
Wolsingham

and

All those mines, quarries, seams and veins of iron,
iron ore and ironstone in part of the parishes of
Stanhope and Wolsingham

Party B

All those mines, quarries,
seams and veins of iron,
iron ore and ironstone in
part of the parish of
Wolsingham

Party C

All those mines, quarries,
seams and veins of iron,
iron ore and ironstone in
part of the parish of
Stanhope

Fig. 1. Summary of the Principal Weardale Mining Leases, c. 1844

'Counsel's opinion is wished as to how far Mr Wilkinson or his lessees can interfere with Mr Beaumont in the workings of the mines or veins wherein exist any materials to which Mr Wilkinson or his lessees are entitled.

Counsel's opinion is wished whether in case he [Beaumont] refused [to co-operate] he could be compelled to come to some arrangement on the subject and it becomes more necessary to know this as should all the minerals found in the veins be brought to the surface the system of working the mines in the parishes of Stanhope and Wolsingham would be quite changed and a new system would have to be adopted.

Counsel's opinion and advice are requested whether there be any remedy at law or equity to compel some equitable arrangement on the subject.'

Rightful Ownership of the Various Iron Ores

Prior to 1840 it was widely accepted that iron occurred only in the form of argillaceous ironstone in the locality, occurring interbedded with the carboniferous sequence; the ironstone was usually in the form of nodules. As described above, about 1844, the minerals siderite and limonite were discovered in extensive quantities within the mineral-bearing veins of upper Weardale, these minerals often occurring as rider ore. Both of these minerals were relatively free from impurities (particularly phosphorus), and as such were ideal for the manufacture of high grade pig-iron. It is perhaps surprising that the iron minerals in the lead veins had not been recognised or commercially exploited previously. However, it must be remembered that mining of lead and its associated silver had been the traditional industry of the dale for centuries and that there was only a small demand for iron until the building of the railways began in earnest throughout the country about this time.

Despite tradition, there were some persons willing to diversify. In truth they had little option for the lead mining rights in Weardale were already leased and there was little chance of obtaining a sublease as the Beaumont family preferred to work their mines themselves with employed labour. Wilkinson, however had agreed to sublease the rights to mine iron ore in the parishes of Stanhope and Wolsingham to three separate parties referred to in the case notes as Parties A, B, and C (the identity of the three parties is given in the Discussion below). Fig. 1 summarises the resultant situation. The leases entitled the individual parties to 'all those mines, quarries, seams and veins of iron, iron ore and ironstone' in specific parts of the two parishes. Additionally, Party A also leased the rights to 'copper, copper ore, tin, tin ore and all other minerals except… all iron and ironstone [which was held by Party A under a separate lease], coal and crow coal, lime and limestone, firestone and fireclay and all mines and quarries of slate, flagstone and freestone [the latter being held in reserve by Wilkinson] in the parishes of Stanhope and Wolsingham'. The alternative occurrences of iron ore (i.e. in the form of siderite and limonite within the mineralised veins) led to the question of rightful ownership of the rights to mine the different forms of iron ore:

'When these leases were granted no minerals were known to exist in any quantity in the said parishes except some lead and the common clay or argillaceous iron stone, and that was the only ironstone contemplated by the parties when the leases of ironstone were entered into.'

Did the subleases encompass the 'new' forms of iron ore and thus entitle each of the three parties to this material, or did Party A have sole rights to the newly discovered iron minerals, siderite and limonite, under his lease for copper, tin and all other minerals as this lease was clearly meant to include all minerals except lead that occurred in the mineralised veins?

'Now a question arises between A, B and C whether A is not entitled to all the minerals found in the veins whatever the minerals contain… Mr Wilkinson grants a lease to A of all mines and seams of copper and tin and other minerals (except certain ones named) throughout the Parishes of Stanhope and Wolsingham. This confers on A a right to claim all minerals to which Mr Beaumont is not entitled and which are not excepted. In working these [copper, tin etc.] A finds in certain veins, but in veins only, substances which are found to contain iron with other matter. B and C then say they are entitled to these as containing iron—now if this be correct it will make the difficulty of working the mines very great inasmuch as the adjusting of the rights of the respective parties will be difficult.'

Now that it was recognised that commercial quantities of iron ore occurred in the lead veins as well as in beds within the carboniferous sequence in the district, Wilkinson apparently wanted to simplify the complex situation for which he was responsible and establish rightful ownership of the 'new' minerals under the various subleases he had granted. A prolonged legal battle between the three sublessees would undoubtedly result in a substantial loss of income for Wilkinson from his mining interests until the issues were resolved—and this at a time when demand for high quality iron was soaring.

The wording in the subleases for iron is definitive 'all… seams and veins of iron, iron ore and ironstone'; from a purely technical point of view there can be no doubt that this clearly encompasses all iron ore in whatever form it occurs and irrespective of its mode of occurrence i.e. whether in beds or mineralised veins, and hence it might appear at first sight that all parties had equal claim upon the ore. Wilkinson, however, was considering the possible legal interpretation of the wording in the leases; were the newly discovered iron minerals excluded from the subleases for iron on the grounds that these minerals were neither known nor contemplated to occur in Weardale at the time the leases were drawn up? The wording in the subleases made no reference to the future discovery of new minerals and the question then arose whether or not a mineral that was unknown (in the area included in the lease) at the time the lease was drawn up could be implied. Party A claimed that the rights to the iron minerals siderite and limonite were held by him under the lease for copper, tin and all other minerals rather than under the lease for iron and ironstone.

'A contends in fact that Mr Beaumont and he as lessee under Mr Wilkinson being entitled to all the substances found in veins, B and C cannot under their leases claim any substances found in the veins, merely on the ground that it contains iron.'

In support of this argument the known occurrence of iron pyrites in the lead veins is cited. Parties B and C had not been granted similar subleases for copper and other minerals and thus, it was maintained, had no claim on the pyrites simply because pyrites contained iron. Indeed it is unlikely that Parties B and C would make any claim on the pyrites as, relative to the ironstone, there was insufficient of the material to be worth working. However, if we interpret the wording in the lease for copper and other minerals literally, it could be argued that Party A himself did not have any claim on the pyrites, as the lease specifically excluded iron: 'except… all iron and ironstone, coal…' etc. The counter argument might be that 'iron and ironstone' meant exactly that—thus by default, Party A was entitled to iron sulphide, pyrites, as this was not listed in the exclusions. However, the interpretation of the actual wording of the leases seems to have been secondary to the intentions implicit when the leases were first agreed. It was contended that there was a legally significant difference between the lease for copper etc. and that for iron in that the former was intended to imply all minerals other than lead that occurred in veins whereas the intention of the latter was to lease the rights to mine the beds of ironstone—this despite the fact that the word 'veins' was included in the iron lease:

'In the lease of copper tin and other minerals to A it is to be observed Mr Wilkinson does not reserve [for himself] a single substance found in veins, at least not then known to exist in veins, but simply things found in beds or quarries. [i.e. ironstone, coal, limestone etc.]

Counsel's opinion is therefore further requested as to the right of B and C under their respective leases to claim any substances found in veins throughout the parishes of Stanhope and Wolsingham under the plea that such substances contain iron.'

The reader may be forgiven at this point for considering the whole situation to be bordering on the ludicrous, but the sheer intensity of the arguments must surely reflect the eagerness of the individual parties to win the rights to the siderite and limonite.

Discussion

Having described the legal aspects of the case, it would be appropriate to address the context in which the arguments arose and to identify those parties arguing over ownership of the subleased iron mining rights.

In the above account the identity of the three parties A, B, and C is most likely Cuthbert Rippon, Charles Attwood, and Thomas Willis respectively. Cuthbert Rippon was a local land-owner in the Stanhope area and Member of Parliament for Gateshead. His son, John, planned the erection of a small blast furnace near Stanhope and this is recorded as being erected in 1845.[8,6] Little is known concerning Thomas Willis but he is believed to have had connections with the Rippon family. The entrepreneurial activities of Charles Attwood on the other hand are well documented.[5]

About the time that the case notes were compiled (1844) Charles Attwood, who subsequently founded the Weardale Iron

Co., had become aware of the existence of extensive siderite/limonite mineralisation in Weardale. Attwood knew from his earlier experiences, his father being an iron master in Shropshire, that these forms of iron ore would produce, on smelting, a pig iron equivalent to the high quality *spiegeleisen* iron produced in Germany and superior to that produced from common ironstone for the purpose of conversion to high quality steel.[5] Attwood approached Wilkinson for a lease to mine this ore in Weardale but found that Wilkinson had already agreed to grant subleases to mine iron ore in parts, but not all, of Stanhope and Wolsingham parishes to Thomas Willis and Cuthbert Rippon.

Attwood had been planning the formation of an iron smelting company for some years previously but had been hampered by the lack of rail facilities connecting the main ironstone body known at that time (in Cleveland) to the coal in Durham.[5] Having discovered the existence of the siderite/limonite mineralisation in Weardale, and presumably begun negotiations with Wilkinson, he had (by May 1844) rented a large section of the Durham coal field at its point closest to Weardale to which area it was to be connected by an extension of the Stanhope and Tyne railway, under construction in 1844 (opened for traffic May 1845 [7]) thereby ensuring a ready supply of fuel for the blast furnaces required for smelting the ore. Attwood was also an accomplished geologist/mineralogist and well able to exploit this knowledge to his advantage. Additionally, he had sought and obtained backing for his proposed Weardale Iron Company from Barings Bank.[5]

It was probably as a result of Attwood's approaches that Wilkinson became aware of the legal complications that might arise from the existence of the different forms of iron ore. Wilkinson himself was a barrister (called to the bar in 1814), Recorder of Newcastle, a Magistrate and subsequently a judge at Durham,[3] it would thus be essential that his business activities should not give rise to questions regarding his judicial integrity and for this reason he was probably responsible for the decision to seek independent legal advice as to the validity of the subleases in question and whether or not a separate lease could be granted for the siderite/limonite.

It is not recorded which of the four parties (Rippon, Willis, Wilkinson or Attwood) first questioned the scope of the iron ore subleases granted to Rippon and Willis but the wealth of circumstantial evidence seems to point to Attwood as the main protagonist as he, after all, had most to lose—the securing of the rights to the Weardale siderite and limonite was the final hurdle he needed to clear in order to ensure the birth of his planned iron smelting company. If at the same time he could eliminate competition then so much the better. Attwood also had extensive geological and mineralogical knowledge, was the most experienced businessman (biographical accounts of Attwood bear witness to his business acumen and successes [5]) and was well-equipped to exploit what he may have considered to be loopholes in the leases in his determination to secure the Weardale siderite/limonite for himself. No doubt Wilkinson was a willing aide for he, as a barrister and pillar of local society, would want to ensure the absolute legality of the situation.

Counsel's opinion on the legal questions has not yet come to light, but the eventual solution to the enigma was in fact simple; Wilkinson would sublease iron rights to the three parties as already agreed, but Rippon and Willis would immediately grant their rights to Attwood, who was in the best position to exploit the full potential of the iron ore, presumably in exchange for an appropriate duty or rent. Thus all parties benefited from the arrangement and arguments about the rightful ownership of the different iron ores evaporated; Rippon and Willis would receive income from their lease without the expense and business risk of setting up their own company to mine and smelt the ore, whilst Attwood achieved his aim of a virtual monopoly of the Weardale iron ore. The solution to the enigma is confirmed by the consecutive dates quoted in the leases. Wilkinson assigned the lease to Rippon and Willis on April 29th 1845, Rippon and Willis then assigned a sublease to Attwood on April 30th 1845.[9]

It then remained for Attwood to agree appropriate working arrangements with the Beaumonts to overcome the final obstacle and ensure unrestricted access to the iron ore. Attwood successfully negotiated an agreement with the Beaumont company which was eventually signed (1847) by Thomas Sopwith,[10] the company mining agent. Under this agreement Attwood was contracted to work the Beaumont mine which was rich in iron minerals (West Pasture Mine in Stanhopeburn) keeping the iron ore for himself but bound over to supply all the lead ore to the Beaumont company in return for a fair price—a most sensible solution given the complexities that might have arisen from dual-partnership working of the mine.

References

1. DRURY J L. in *Boles and Smeltmills,* Eds. Willies L, & Cranstone D. (The Historical Metallurgy Society Ltd., 1992), 22,

2. RAISTRICK A, & JENNINGS B. *A History of Lead Mining in the Pennines* (Longmans, 1965).

3. Durham Year Book for 1859.

4. Manuscript in author's possession.

5. JEANS J S. *Pioneers of the Cleveland Iron Trade* (H. G. Reid, 1875), Chapter 1 'Charles Attwood'.

6. Epitome of Weardale Iron Co. leases, dated 1865, in private possession.

7. EGGLESTONE W M. All Around Stanhope, 130.

8. SNAITH A F & LEE E C. The Railway Magazine, (1942), Vol. 88, 198.

9. HEYES W F. *The Bonny Moor Hen* (Journal of the Weardale Field Study Society, 1997), No. 9, 21–31 .

10. Durham County Records Office, Document Ref. NCB14/4.

Lancelot Allgood and Mary Loraine

R A Fairbairn

Summary

In his own time Sir Lancelot Allgood was a man of considerable standing, yet today his deep involvement in the lead mining industry of Alston Moor during the eighteenth century is rarely mentioned. Fortunately some of his papers, as well as those of Mrs Mary Loraine, are preserved in Northumberland Records Office. By combining these papers with other sources an outline of their activities has been constructed, though much detail is still missing. Most of their mining activity was centred upon the Nent Valley, they smelted their ores at Allendale and Blackhall Mills.

Sir Lancelot Allgood[1]

Son and heir of Isaac Allgood of Brandon White House near Beamish, Lancelot married on the 22nd February 1739, Jane Allgood, daughter of Robert Allgood of Nunwick. Through his marriage he inherited the Nunwick estate, which is still the home of the Allgoods. In fact he may have made little monetary gain as Robert had been deeply in debt to George Allgood his brother, owing him £2,400. The debt was caused by George taking on the cost of several lawsuits on behalf of his brother. Robert was unwilling or unable to settle his debt to George. In a will of 7th September 1727 George bequeathed his Chipchase estate and Birtley tithes to his friend Lancelot Allgood and Henry Quentry, vintner of Bermondsey to be sold to pay off his debts, including a £3,000 mortgage and discharged him of his debt of £2,400.[2]

At the time of the 1745 rebellion Lancelot was Sheriff of Northumberland. He was present at the reception given for the Duke of Cumberland in Newcastle, when the Duke was given the freedom of the City.

In the 1747–8 Parliamentary elections he stood as the Tory candidate, and won the seat. The result of the election was; Allgood 982, Lord Ossulston 971, but the sheriff rejected 27 of the Tory votes and declared Lord Ossulston the winner. Mr Allgood petitioned Parliament, but the dispute remained unresolved until a year later when Lord Ossulston withdrew his claim.

During his relatively short parliamentary career, he did not stand in the 1754 elections, Lancelot was very active in promoting several turnpike acts for local roads, including the bill authorising the repair and widening of the road from Alnmouth to Hexham. He served on committees for other turnpikes being progressed by Sir William Middleton.

In 1760 Mr Allgood was knighted upon the accession of George III. His eldest daughter, Hannah, married William, later Sir William Loraine. His second daughter, Isabella, married Lambton Loraine, brother of William. Sir Lancelot was succeeded by his son James in 1786.

Mary Loraine

Mary was the wife of Robert Loraine of Beaufront Woodhead, who was buried at St John Lee on the 23rd February 1761.[3] Mary Loraine died January 8th 1779 aged 63.[4] The Loraine family was a prosperous Tynedale family, the relationship of Robert to the branch headed by Sir William Loraine of Kirkharle is not known, but Sir William did have five sons. The relationship between the Allgoods and Loraines has already been noted.

The economic background

Throughout the first half of the eighteenth century there was political unrest. Many of the Northumbrian gentry supported the Stuarts in the 1715 rebellion, some losing their land as a result. The most spectacular loss was that of the Radcliffes, who lost all their estates including Alston Moor to the Crown, Lord Derwentwater being beheaded for his part in the rising. The Crown gave his estates to the Greenwich Hospital. The lead industry was so depressed that the Allendale forest grieveship inhabitants petitioned at the Quarter Sessions of July 1711, to have the poor cess paid jointly with other Allendale grieveships, so that the burden of out of work miners would be shared,

'Therefore your poor petitioners humbly pray that as the whole parish hath had the advantage of the mines when that trade flourished your worships will be pleased to order that we may be equal in our sufferings now when it seems to decline'.[5]

For the first half of the century the price of lead was almost static at £12 per ton. The price then rose to about £17 per ton, which held through the 60s and into the 70s with a short collapse to £12 per ton around 1760. Prices fell during the 70s back to £12 per ton by 1780 then recovered to £20 per ton for most of the rest of the century.[6]

Under these circumstances it was not impossible to make profit, the London Lead Company built up its business to a point where it was one of the major companies in the region during the nineteenth century. However others failed, Colonel George Liddell leased the Alston Moor mines in 1736, but by 1745 his enterprises had failed. Similarly the Earl of Carlisle and Company, who took extensive leases on Alston Moor, started their operations in 1771 and sold their interests to the London Lead Company in 1798.

Losses inevitably shook the confidence of investors, a memorandum from Thomas Ramsay thought to have been written in about 1782 reflects the spirit of the times;

'Lead mining business in Aldstone Moor seems rather upon the decline for many lessees are quite tired out by the great expense attending them—particularly the Newcastle people who for some years past were very great adventurers but are now it is said given up for they find the hopes their agents gave generally miscarried. ... Out of 200 or 300 leases of mines, not more than three or four show a profit and last year scarce any but the Quakers Company (The London Lead Company) did well'.[7]

The economic relationship of Lancelot Allgood and Mary Loraine

It is not clear what the precise relationship was. In the case of their workings in Thorngill they were equal partners sharing all costs, dividing the ore equally between them. In selling her leases to Sir Lancelot, Mary Loraine may have just been reducing her involvement in the mines, wishing to be free of the disputes that had arisen over the working of Caplecleugh and Cowslitts. It seems that they were very willing to cooperate with each other, but were equally keen to preserve their independence.

The mines

Sharpley Mine

Most of the mines involving Sir Lancelot Allgood are situated on Alston Moor, the exception is Sharpley Mine (NY 879 723),[8] which is on his own land about one mile SSE of Simonburn in the North Tyne valley. Sharpley Mine was worked for a short period, possibly only 1750–51, and though the ore was good there was not sufficient quantity to make it pay. The ore was smelted at Sir Walter Blackett's Dukesfield Smelt Mill one mile east of Whitley chapel. Only about 4.75 tons of lead are known to have been produced.

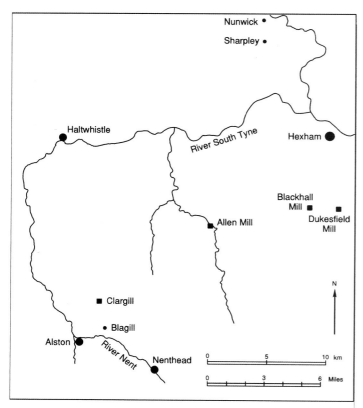

Fig. 1. Locations

The Alston Moor Mines

Caplecleugh, Cowhill, Cowslitts and Hangingshaw Veins

The veins are on the west side of the River Nent above Nenthead. The documents relating to these mines illustrate the legal complexity that could arise in mine leases.

It is convenient to start the story with the Greenwich Hospital demising a lease of Caplecleugh Vein and Caplecleugh Cross Vein to Susannah Emerson, widow of Joseph Emerson, on 3rd July 1751.[9] This indenture only confirmed ownership of an earlier 21-year lease given in 1747, and thus Susannah only had a 17-year lease to sell. Robert Loraine and Dr Ralph Tatham

agreed on the 24th August 1752 to be equal partners to work the veins, and Susannah assigned the residue of the lease to them for £200. Ralph Tatham was a 'doctor in physick' of Sunderland, he died soon after entering the partnership leaving his share of the mine to Ralph Lambton and George Scruton upon trust to sell it for payment of his debts. Lambton and Scruton refused to prove the will or act upon it, Elizabeth Tatham, obtained administration of the goods of Ralph but died before disposing of the share of lease. The half share was then possessed by Joseph Yellowley administrator of the late Dr Loraine. Joseph Yellowley and Mary Loraine agreed to a partnership, but on the 2nd October Mary bought Joseph Yellowley's share for £430. The sale included a half share of Smitter Gill Hill and a part share in Carr's Vein, Rampgill Head and Nentsberry Haggs Veins.

Mary sold her leases of Caplecleugh, and Caplecleugh Cross Vein to Sir Lancelot Allgood on the 11th October 1762. This transaction is summarised in an indenture which also cites an agreement made with John Errington for the sum of £1,200 in settlement of all the demands upon the late Robert Loraine and an agreement made by Sir Lancelot with Mary Loraine for the purchase of the two leases of £1,200 (i.e. paying off her husband's debts) and all her costs of suit with John Errington and the sum of £300 for transferring the leases of Caplecleugh Sun Vein and Caplecleugh West End, and for lead ore lying at bank at Caplecleugh mined since Lady Day. Further Sir Lancelot was to pay the men that raised the ore.[10]

The position of the working is not clear, there is a deep level which was driven by Loraine and Tatham at about the horizon of the Little Limestone NY 7873 4260 towards the Caplecleugh Veins. Mary Loraine was driving a level from a shaft sunk ahead of the deep level. Mary held the lease for all of Caplecleugh vein. Caplecleugh Sun Vein was held under a lease granted to Loraine and Tatham. The veins carried ore at two main horizons, the Firestone sill and the Great Limestone. The Firestone Sill deposits were worked from shafts, the main one being Caplecleugh Engine shaft, but these deposits were probably almost worked out by middle of the eighteenth century. This left the Great Limestone and the deep level of Loraine and Tatham probably intended to exploit this strata by sumps, but it would encounter higher strata as it crossed Caplecleugh Vein, thus access to the Great Limestone would become more difficult, with the expected problems of drainage. When Sir Lancelot took the lease in 1762 he was obviously aware of this and he considered various methods of working the veins. He considered making a level from Old Cowslitts Vein workings to Caplecleugh Engine Shaft in the shale above the Great Limestone, with the assertion that the water would be taken away in the chinks of the limestone. The second proposal seems to be to carry forward Loraine and Tatham's level to Caplecleugh Engine Shaft. The third suggestion was to drive a level out of Old Carr's Low Level, thus starting below the Great Limestone. His estimated costs of the three alternatives were £1,363, £1,354 and £7,480. As the lease was to terminate in 1768 Sir Lancelot requested the Greenwich Hospital to grant him a new, 21-year, lease.[11] The outcome of this request is not known. Dickinson's report of 1821 noted that Caplecleugh Veins had raised a great quantity of ore in almost all the sills as deep as the Great Limestone, they were rich in the Great

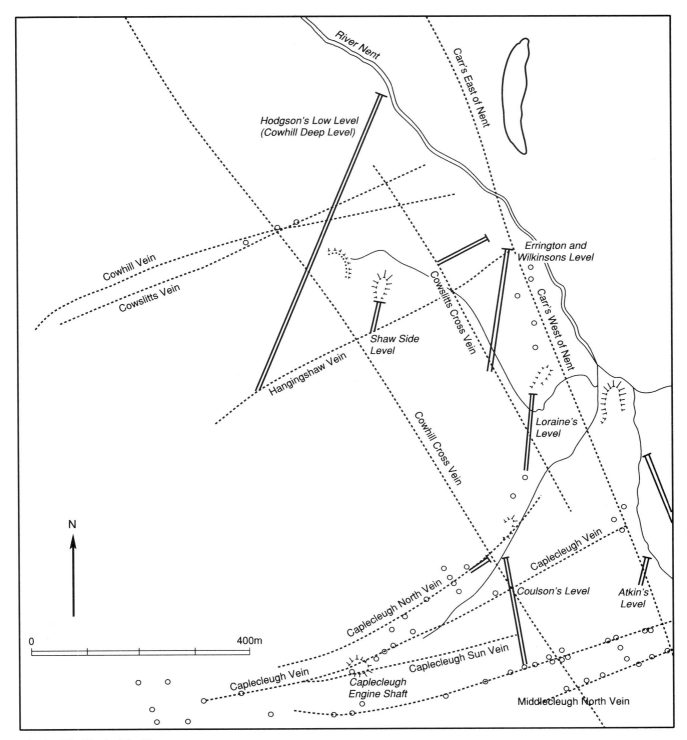

Fig. 2. The Head of the Nent

Limestone east from the Engine Shaft, but to the west of that shaft they became poor and were much troubled by water. The latter length was left for the London Lead Company to work by its Caplecleugh Horse Level, NY 7811 4349, that was driven from Brigal Burn.

Sir Lancelot was faced with a problem for he had purchased the ore that had been raised prior to his purchase but he did not have a smelt mill, he offered the ore to the Greenwich Hospital ore at 54 shillings a bing, the response was negative, with the classic comment 'Lead is plenty and the demand very slack' and 'desire Sr Lan't would offer it as low as he is Determined to Sell at'.[12] He overcame the problem by purchasing a half share in Blackhall Mill.

Now it may well be asked where John Errington entered the equation. The documents preserved in the Northumberland Records Office appear to offer a complete picture, but of course they do not give the other side. Thomas Errington was farmer of the mines of the Earl of Derwentwater, he was in partnership with Enoch Hudson. As Thomas went out in support of the Stuart cause the family would have problems after the 1715 rebellion. Errington and Adam Wilkinson formed a partnership or company, and on the 18th June 1754 Adam applied for a lease of Caplecleugh North Vein.[13] At this point it is necessary to note the way leases worked, the lease was for 1,200 yards with 40 yards on each side of the vein. The lease included the right to work the 80 yards length of any vein that crosses through the lease. The earliest lease takes precedence, similarly when two veins converged so that one entered the 40 yd width of the other, the older lease should have precedence. For quite a lot of its length the Caplecleugh North Vein lies just over 40 yards off Caplecleugh Vein, but to the west the veins converge, the 1747 lease of Caplecleugh Vein being owned by Mary Loraine.

The confusion regarding the lease of Cowslitts Vein probably starts in 1737 when Colonel George Liddell gained almost all the Alston Moor leases, in his records he notes against Cowslitts

'Uncertain how She runs. Q'ry was not She joined to yᵉ Carrs for Mr Hale. She is on the West Side of Nent just opposite to the Carrs. There are Some workmen have offered to Raise Oar per bing for 25*s* and Mr E has bidd 21*s* & let he so'.[14]

The probability is that Mr E is Mr John? Errington. It is believed that the leases of Thomas Errington passed on to John, then to William his son, and thus to Henry nephew of William, thus the question of which Errington may not be important. Old Carr's west of Nent Vein cuts across Hangingshaw Vein and may also cut Cowslitts, the boundary between Carr's east and west of Nent being the River Nent just about where Cowslitts and Cowhill veins reach the Nent. The lease of Carr's West of Nent was held by Mary Loraine and would be the basis for a claim to the 80 yd length where it crosses Caplecleugh, Hangingshaw and possibly Cowhill and Cowslitts. Mary also had the lease of Cowhill Cross Vein from 1747, this would enable her to claim 80 yards of Cowhill, Cowslitts and Hangingshaw and Caplecleugh veins. Sir Lancelot Allgood purchased the lease of Old Cowslitts Vein from Ann Armstrong, Christopher Bell and Elizabeth Blenkinsop on the 27th February 1762, with the restriction he was not allowed to hush.

It is now clear that there were plenty of areas of conflict. There was a lot of money involved in the Cowslitts dispute. According to Mr Hewitson's (agent for Mary Loraine) report written on the 19th November 1764

'Cowslits is all fresh ground and now wrought by 36 men Each Bargain 6 men which is all hopeful and Laid Open in Length 80 fathom and Raising Ore pretty well, She turned out Last Year by 18 men working 275 Bing 2 Horse. She is now laid open boath by shaft & sumps which was a dead charge upon the Grove Last Year'.

A sketch of the workings indicate that they were at the north end of the vein, i.e. between Cowslitts Cross Vein and the Nent. The sketch also indicates that Adam Elliot and Errington had started to sink a sump ahead of the Loraine workings. Comments on the sketch say that 'Elliot and Errington has set on to Sink a Sump into the Same Vein of Loraine's at Cowslitts which they have no Right to Sink any Sump or Sumps in the S'd Vein, because there Grant of Ground is for an East West Vein which is Supposed to Cross Cow Slit Vein', i.e. Cowslitts Cross Vein?

Fortunately there is an independent source of information regarding these workings. This was written by Joseph Hilton in 1778. At this point it should be noted that Hilton had a very poor opinion of Errington and Wilson and would naturally be biased against them. His account states that Errington and Wilkinson's 'first trial was for Caplecleugh North Vein and had they met with that vein and nothing else, there would soon have been an end of their works, but instead of meeting with Caplecleugh North Vein they cut Cowslitts Cross Vein which had a piece of good ore in the Little Limestone; they could not work her with advantage there and consequently run her point northward, hoping to find her in the Great Limestone where it was near the surface, but instead of that sunk directly upon Hangingshaw which turned out very good. The appearance of Old Works at Cowslitts induced them to engage that Ground, and Mrs Loraine's pretended claim to a right there forced those Works to be proceeded with and has brought them a good deal of Profit'. According to the Dickinsons, Errington and Wilkinson raise a great quantity of ore from the Cowhill, Cowslitts and Hangingshaw Veins but as they worked to the west they became poor. They also say that Errington and Wilkinson drove Cowhill Deep Level as far as Hangingshaw Vein. It seems that Mary Loraine and Sir Lancelot lost this argument, though why is not obvious.

Errington and Wilkinson continued their level along Cowslitts Cross Vein up to their Caplecleugh North Vein lease.

A list of leases[15] granted to Henry Hetherington written in 1880 gives the boundary of the various leases:

	yds	
Caple Cleugh	940	Westw'd & 250 yards Eastward from the Engine Shaft
Caple Cleugh Sun Vein	1200	Do from the Boundary Shaft sunk for the said Vein
Caple Cleugh North Vein	1200	Do from Middle Cleugh Runner
Caple Cleugh Cross Vein	700	Northward from a Line drawn East and West from Caple Cleugh Sun Vein Boundary
Cowshills	1200	Westward from Nent River
Cowshills Cross Vein	300	Southw'd & 900 Northward from Caple Cleugh Burn
Cowhill	1200	Westw'd from the Boundary of Carrs West if Nent
Hangingshaw East End		From Nent River to Rampgill Burn
Hangingshaw Cross Vein		From Rampgill Burn to a Line drawn Eastward from the foot of Small Cleugh Syke to Killhope Cross
Carrs East of Nent		From Nent River to Rampgill Burn
Hangingshaw Vein		From the West Boundary of Carrs West of Nent to the East Boundary of Caple Cleugh Cross Vein

The name Hetherington is a mistake for Errington as it is associated with articles of agreement dated 4th Oct. 1800 in which Henry Errington with Robert Hodgson of Alston, James Shoot of London, Joseph Liddell of Moorhouse, Carlisle and William Bell of Carlisle, sold the lease of these veins to the London Lead Company.

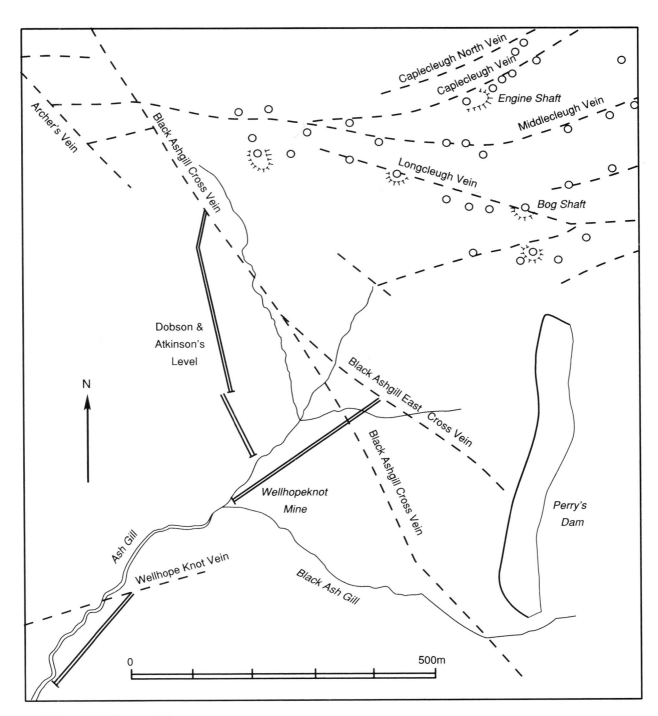

Fig. 3.   The Nent–Ashgill watershed

Old Carr's Vein

The vein was among those purchased by Mary Loraine from Joseph Yellowley in 1762. She leased the vein to a partnership of John Hutchinson of Nentsberry Greens, a half share, John Hind of Crook Bank and Alexander Thompson of Alston a quarter share each. The vein had been worked long ago in the Great Limestone, but because the ore occurred in flats it is very difficult to decide when a vein is worked out.

The trustees of Mary Loraine sold the Old Carr's West of Nent for £205 to a company of eight working miners who made a success of working the mine, so much so that it was credited as being instrumental in John and Utrick Walton of Nest and John Dowson becoming 'great mining adventurers'.[16]

John Dickinson described a very good flat that he saw in this mine

'which was more than four yards wide and three feet thick in the middle and two feet at the sides, all lying nearly loose. The ore had seemingly been formed both from the roof and the sole of the flat until the one in the roof had grown too heavy and dropped down upon the other so that there was a flat limestone roof and a space of a foot or half a yard between it and the ore, so that one might have seen over the ore for several fathoms in length. The workmen raised ore in that flat for three quarters of a year at six shillings per bing'. [17]

John was Moormaster at the beginning of the nineteenth century, so it seems that the mine could still deliver riches long after Mary Loraine's time.

Black Ashgill Veins and Caplecleugh West End

The Greenwich Hospital leased the vein known as North of Black Ashgill to William Dobson and George Atkinson, for 21 years from 19th December 1756.

The partners sold three-quarters of the lease on the 15th September 1760,[18] dividing the shares between William Dobson of Dryburn (situated between Alston and Garrigill), George Atkinson and Thomas Bland of Garrigill Gate, Anthony Pratt of Eggleston (near Blanchland), John Emerson and George Wallis of Hotts in the parish of Stanhope, Jacob Lowes, Joseph Lowes, Thomas Dobson and William Dobson all of the parish of Stanhope. The price was five shillings each, and the share were divided thus:

Thomas Bland	one eighth
Anthony Pratt	one eighth
John Emmerson	one sixteenth
George Wallis	one sixteenth
Jacob Lowes	one eighth
Joseph Lowes	one eighth
Thomas Dobson	one sixteenth
William Dobson	one sixteenth

All the partners were to contribute to the cost of working the vein in proportion to their shares in the company, to be paid within three months of notice being given in writing by five of the partners, 'whose right and Title shall be five Eighths shares'. In the event of a shareholder failing to pay, his shares will be forfeit to the other shareholders, and all rights to the vein lost to him. No expenditure or work was to be started without the consent of five of the partners as previously defined.

W Dobson and G Atkinson were to be employed at the mine, being paid 'Common Customary Wages' or employ two workmen in their place. If more than two workmen were required then the other shareholders could employ men in proportion to their shareholding.

There were also restrictions on any of the partners taking leases within the boundary of the level or crossing it, any new tack or grant to be shared between all shareholders.

The partners were to elect one person only to manage the affairs of the mine and the affairs relating to it, the majority required was to be equal of five eighths of the shares.

An indenture of the 23rd September 1762[19] records the lease of a Cross Vein at Black Eshgillhead to William Dobson from 24th June for 21 years at ⅕th duty. A note on the back of this indenture records that the lease was sold to Sir Lancelot Allgood of Nunwick for five shillings. Wm. Dobson having previously sold all his rights to Sir Lancelot Allgood.

A lengthy indenture of the 28th December 1763[20] records an agreement between Ann Pratt, widow of Anthony Pratt, and Sir Lancelot Allgood. It cites the various transactions concerning the North of Black Ashgill Vein:

'23rd September 1762—The Greenwich Hospital leased a Cross Vein at Black-Esh-Gill-Head, to William Dobson of Bridge End for 21 years from the 24th June 1761.'

As time went by various partners sold off their shares, suggesting that the mine was not a success. Ann Pratt inherited Anthony Pratt's estate including a ⅜th share of the mine. This included the share originally owned by George Atkinson and Thomas Bland and bought by Pratt. Ann Pratt sold her ⅜th share to Sir Lancelot Allgood for £90 on the 28th December 1763.

An indenture of the 3rd June 1763[21], records the sale by Jacob Lowes, Joseph Lowes, John Emerson and George Wallis to Sir Lancelot Allgood their ⅜th share of the lease of North of Black Esh Gill Vein and a Cross Vein at Black Esh Gill Head for the sum of £90.

Having got all the shares he was free to work the ground which he did with the objective of trying Caplecleugh West End. He extended the trial begun by Dobson and Atkinson in Black Ashgill to Caplecleugh West End.

Wellhopeknot Vein

Sir Lancelot Allgood purchased the lease of the vein from Mary Loraine in 1762[22] and renewed the lease for 21 years at one fifth duty in 1766.[23] No information regarding his workings are available.

Thorngill and Lough

The veins run along the north side of the Nent Valley between Alston and Blagill. How the leases came into the possession of Allgood and Loraine is not known. Mr Hewitson reported to Mary Loraine in 1761 that Thorngill and Lough had been worked in the past by the 'old man' above the random level, and did not think this region to be worth a trial. He had sunk two sumps under the level into fresh sills and driven for ten fathoms from each sump without meeting with any encouragement. Despite his disappointment the trials must have continued for by 1766 considerable quantities of ore were being produced, e.g. 1765 10 bing, 1766 1606 bings, 1767 1970 bings, all the ore after 1765 was shared equally between Sir Lancelot and Mary. No mention is made of Blagill Smelt Mill that was situated near one of the levels to Thorngill Vein, it is assumed that it was derelict by then.

The Smelt Mills

Smelt Mill near Clargill

A draft of a petition[24] from Sir Lancelot Allgood to the Commissioners of the Greenwich Hospital is available. The mill was to have been built at Trout-in-Well near Clargill on the Common of Alston Moor. This location is not known, and there is no evidence it was built. He requested a twenty-one year lease with the liberty to cut and win peat and limestone from the common, and permission to remove bellows and furnishings from the mill on completion of the lease. He estimated the cost of making the mill to be in excess of six hundred pounds. He was willing to pay a 'Small rent'.

Blackhall Smelt Mill[25] NY 932 584

Sir Lancelot Allgood purchased a half share of the mill on the 26th February 1762. He retained his share until 21st November 1780 when he sold his half share to Robert Vasie and Anthony Hewitson. Who owned the other half share is not known but it may well have been Mary Loraine. By 1765 it is fairly certain that Mary had control of the mill, paying taxes and the blacksmith. An indenture of 21st November 1780 states that the mill had been in the possession of Robert and Mary Loraine and was by that time held by George Loraine. All of Mary Loraine's ore was smelted at the mill.

In 1765 Sir Lancelot was using one of the two ore hearths at the mill. There are records of Mary Loraine smelting her ore at the mill from 1770 to 1778.

Allen Mill[26] NY 8312 5660

The lease of the mill was transferred from Mr Bacon to Sir Lancelot Allgood in 1766. The handover was very amicable, Mr Bacon allowing the use of one of the hearths by Sir Lancelot when he was not requiring it, Sir Lancelot paying the costs.[27] The mill had two hearths, and was renovated by Sir Lancelot. Considerable quantities of ore were smelted there, e.g. 220 tons of lead were dispatched from the mill in 1767. There is a gap in the history of the mill between Sir Lancelot's death in 1786, and 1795 when the Blackett Beaumont Company took it over.

References

1. WELFORD, R. *Men of Mark Twixt Tyne and Tweed* (1895), Vol 1, 40–42
2. HINDS, A B. *A History of Northumberland* (1896), Vol 9, 70
3. NRO ZAL 1/2
4. HINDS, A B. *A History of Northumberland* (1896), Vol 3, 199
5. HINDS, A B. *A History of Northumberland* (1896), Vol 3, 11
6. SMITH S. *Special Report on the Mineral Resources of Great Britain* (1923), Vol XXV, Plate 3
7. NRO A68a Howard Family Documents
8. FAIRBAIRN, R A. 'The Cost of Producing Lead From Sharpley Mine in Northumberland During the 18th Century'. *British Mining* (1992), No. 45, 28–31
9. NRO ZAL 89/7
10. NRO ZAL 56/1
11. NRO ZAL 89/7
12. NRO ZAL 1/2
13. WALLACE, W. (1890), 120
14. LIDDELL, G. ADM 79 35 p 3
15. Durham Record Office D/Bo/B10
16. DICKINSON, J. & T., (1821), 195
17. *ibid.*
18. NRO ZAL 1/2/6
19. NRO ZAL 1/2/5
20. NRO ZAL 1/2/9
21. NRO ZAL 1/2/10
22. NRO ZAL 1/2/4
23. NRO ZAL 1/2/1
24. NRO ZAL 1/2
25. FAIRBAIRN, R A. 'An 18th Century Lead Smelt Mill at Blackhall, Hexhamshire, Northumberland'. *British Mining* (1991), No. 43, 47–52
26. FAIRBAIRN, R A. 'The Mines of Alston Moor'. *British Mining* (1993), No. 47, 169–172
27. NRO ZAL 56/1

Early Barytes Mining at the Cowgreen Group of Mines including Dubby Sike and Isabella

Harold L. Beadle

It was often said by local miners that there was some mystery in connection with the beginning of the mining and dressing of barytes at these mines. A view which I, at one time, shared until after I began to research mining in Upper Teesdale. However, it must be said that there is no disputing the view that the demand for the product was exceedingly small for some reason until the 1890s when there was a change. For years before this there were several well known veins in which there was abundant easily won ore, but they were remote and there was no access for wheeled vehicles until the late 1870s, and no railway to Middleton-in-Teesdale over ten miles away until 1868. However, soon after that the Duke of Cleveland, in order to make the area more attractive to those who wanted to mine for minerals, which were principally lead and barytes, constructed a new road which began a short distance beyond Harwood Beck bridge and finally, when complete, connected with the road leading from Greenhurth Mine to the Alston road on Yad Moss. Before this, the road leading to Harwood followed Sand Sike up to the middle of Low Fell where it turned right and ascended the bank to Peghorn Lodge. Evidence of buildings, presumably dwellings of some sort, could be seen by the side of the old road some fifty or sixty years ago which by now seem to have almost disappeared. It may now be seen why the Cowgreen mines could not compete with places such as Lunehead where production began in 1884, and many others which were more favourably placed near to good roads and the railway and, in most cases, much nearer to the markets.

The possibility that the working of the veins in the area for barytes could be regarded as a profitable undertaking, is claimed by Charles Kneebone in the report he prepared for the Dubby Sike Mining Company Ltd. in 1874, who proposed to mine the Dubby Sike Vein for lead. Kneebone had already drawn attention that a good road was in the course of construction between Langdon Beck and Dubby Sike which would greatly add to all the other advantages outlines and ends with the following,

'Barytes. This mineral abounds and several thousand tons can be made marketable from Dubby Sike Vein. I estimate the barytes can be quarried from the vein, washed and put into carts for 4s 0d per ton, cartage to Middleton Station 10s 6d, or say, F.O. trucks at Middleton at 15s 0d per ton. But if you were to erect a mill near to the River Tees, and make it marketable, I consider it will have a large margin for profit'.[1]

There is abundant evidence that all the veins in the area under consideration had been worked to some extent for lead by the numerous individuals, partnerships and companies who had been engaged there in earlier days, and that as a result of their operations there were many heaps of barytes here and there which had been left by them, needing little work to be made marketable, when the opportunity arose, which appears to have been 1892 with one small exception when in 1872

J. H. Robinson and Company produced a small amount which was probably just another of Robinson's failed ventures.[2]

Teesdale Mineral Company Limited (Backhouse)

The Teesdale Mineral Company Ltd. is recorded as having been in possession of Cowgreen for the years 1892 to 1896, during which they set up a washing and dressing plant on the north bank of Wheelhead Sike, a short distance below the road at NY 809 309. The main purpose was to use up the heaps of barytes which were lying here and there left behind by the earlier lead miners, though it is possible that there was also a small amount of mining in the adjacent vein. The site was well known by the Hedworth Barium miners (referred to later) and also by the author who could still identify the foundations of the oblong dressing floor which was said to have included a building, until they disappeared during the last period of working which ended in 1954. It was not unusual for the man behind the formation of a company or partnership to have his name attached to it, particularly by the local folk. John Church Backhouse, who formed the company, was a member of the well-known family, J. Backhouse and Company, Bankers, Darlington, and he had been actively engaged in lead mining at both Langdon and High Skears during the last half of the nineteenth century. However, lead mining was in decline and it may well be that as a last venture he turned his attention to barytes which by then was being sought after in the district. Always known as 'Backhouse's Rake', its beginning is well documented.

'On Wednesday last, some of the Directors of the Teesdale Mineral Company met at Cow Green Mine for the purpose of starting the new Barytes crushing machinery. The motive power is produced by one of the celebrated oil engines, by Messrs Priestman Bros., of Hull, which gives prospect of success.'

Later, in the evening, the employees were entertained to tea at which there were speeches and good wishes expressed for the success of the new venture.[3] Until then no one in Upper Teesdale had ever thought of employing the internal combustion engine in preference to the whim and the waterwheel! Though there is evidence that steam had been employed at some of the mines. Whether or not the new venture was a success is debatable, having regard to the fact that the recorded output for four years was only 530 tons (see note on oil engine).

The Hedworth Barium Co Limited
(1 St Nicholas Buildings, Newcastle upon Tyne)

When the company was formed is unknown to me. However, it was headed by Jas. C. Rollin, and was in possession of Cowgreen mine in 1898. That it took over from the previous company is not without some confirmation which came from the Hedworth Barium miners, some of whom had worked for Backhouse. It is also clear that the company obtained from the royalty owners a lease which included Cowgreen, Dubby Sike,

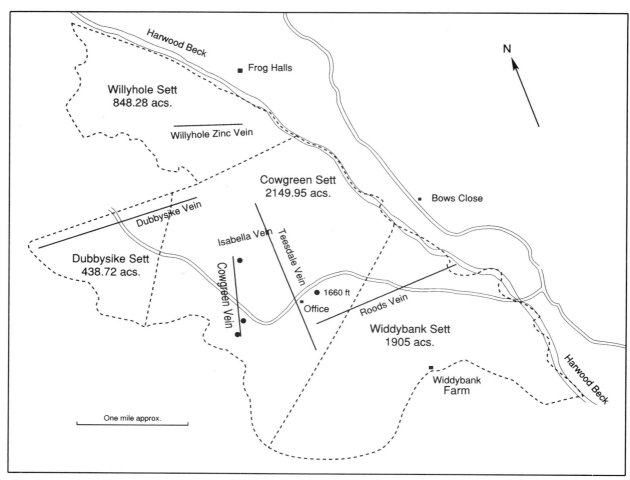

Map showing Cow Green group of mining setts, Dubby Sike and Isabella veins
From an original which does seem to contain some errors. Editor

Widdybank and Willyhole Setts, and that the mines were intensely worked with the exception of Widdybank where there was a good deal of opencasting but no deep mining.[4]

One of the first operations was to drive the Low Level at Cowgreen (NY 811 306) to work the Longband Vein (later called Winterhush Vein). The product from this level was trammed a short distance to the washing rake where it was dressed entirely by hand and deposited onto a large bunning from where it was collected by the carting contractors. Later, two shafts were sunk a short distance apart to a depth of ten fathoms, in order to command lower ground, and a shed was erected over the most westerly one which housed a twelve foot diameter waterwheel which not only drove the machinery which consisted of a crusher, screen and two jiggers, but also the friction-drive hoist which raised the kibble in the shaft. In addition, standing high above the building was a windmill which was geared to a cast iron Cornish lifting pump which extended down the same shaft. The high-grade ore drawn from the shaft was trammed to the washing rake whilst any low-grade was directed to the mill. The other shaft was used as a laddered waygate in which was also installed another pump similar to the one described above, driven by a six foot diameter waterwheel which was set some distance from the shaft on lower ground in order that it could re-use the water from the tail race of the large one. This meant that the power from the wheel had to be transferred some twenty yards by rods

supported by spears which was a well known method in use at that time (see drawings). There was also a small washing rake situated between the low level mouth and its rake at which there was a hotching tub. It was here that any lumps of barytes containing lead, from any of the mines, were brought to be separated.

Dubby Sike Mine (NY 795 319)

Whatever criticism there may have been made in connection with Kneebone's report on the prospects of mining for lead at Dubby Sike in 1874, his assessment and claim that with ease large quantities of barytes could be obtained was not exaggerated. Dubby proved to be a most prolific producer and made a very valuable contribution to the total of the product credited to Cowgreen as a whole, which rose from 380 tons in 1898 to 5231 tons in 1909, after which it began to fall back. Apart from that produced from the opencasts on the higher ground towards the east, of which there is still some evidence, there was nothing more than a level which was driven in from the roadside at an angle until, in a very short distance, it reached the wide vein after which it was possible to command a rapidly rising hill side with great potential for development, which was abundantly proved to be correct in later years. The barytes was trammed from the level mouth a short distance across the road to the washing rake where it was dressed entirely by hand and barrowed onto a large bunning ready to be loaded into the carts.

120

Jackson Dowson, Harold Staley and Tommy Divine with Barytes Carts about 1910

Horses and carts loaded with barytes being carried from Cowgreen to Middleton-in-Teesdale station. Photographed passing through the plantations above High Force.

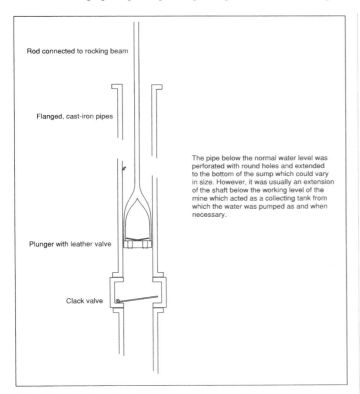

Rod connected to rocking beam

Flanged, cast-iron pipes

The pipe below the normal water level was perforated with round holes and extended to the bottom of the sump which could vary in size. However, it was usually an extension of the shaft below the working level of the mine which acted as a collecting tank from which the water was pumped as and when necessary.

Plunger with leather valve

Clack valve

Cornish pump (not to scale)

Isabella Mine (NY 815 317)

Isabella could never be described in any other way than being remote, being located as it is on the slopes of Sour Mere Rigg overlooking the lower part of the valley of Harwood, and has never been connected by a road to either Harwood or Cowgreen. Tradition has it that the lead produced there was sledged down the valley of Bink Sike to Peg Horn Lane, as was also barytes, until the Hedworth Barium Company ran a railway around the hillside following the contour of the hill until it reached a rise from Hopkins Mine, down which the ore was tipped to be brought out of Hopkins level and washed and dressed at Cow Rake. There were good reports of the quantity and quality of the ore and according to the mine plan, substantial reserves still remain. However, there has been no attempt to mine there since 1922.

East Cowgreen

East Cowgreen may be a little more complex than at first thought, covering as it does a fairly large area mainly on the right side of the road as it ascends to Cowgreen, extending for half a mile in which can be traced three veins, Holmes, Middle and Hopkins which eventually intersect with the Teesdale vein which crosses the road just below the site of the old mineshop, the workings of which can be traced for a long distance in both directions. According to the miners of which my father (1883–1969) was one, though he was not employed by the company until 1900, all the veins were worked for barytes but Hopkins was the only one which was a good producer. However, Cowrake did play quite an important part towards the end of the Hedworth Barium period.

Transport

Transport was always a problem. For a long period the barytes was carried to Middleton-in-Teesdale station by horses and carts, during which there were at least two attempts to employ more advanced methods, neither of which proved to be successful. The first seems to have been in 1902 when it was reported that the Newcastle Company who were working at Cowgreen was trying to convey their mineral by means of a light traction engine.[5] Later there was another attempt to use a steam wagon for the same purpose, but mainly because of the state of the road and the fact that the wagon had narrow smooth

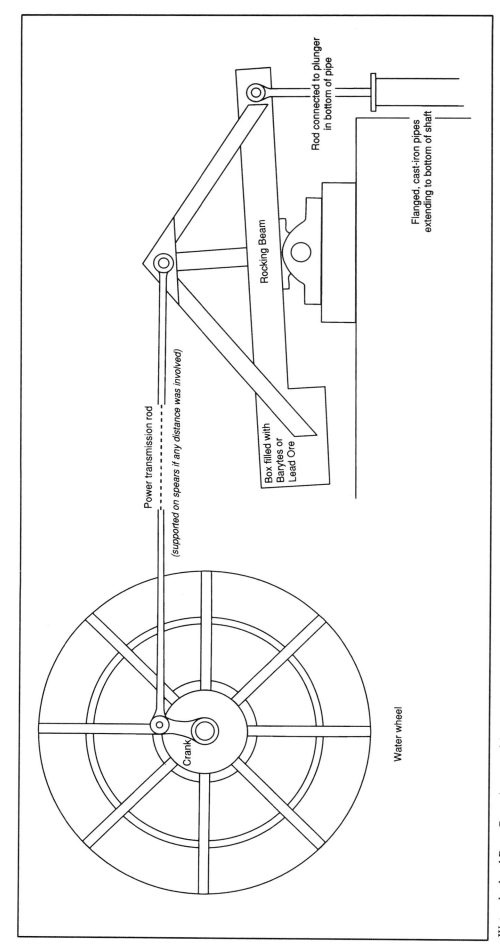

Waterwheel and Beam Pump (not to scale).

122

Foden steam wagon photographed at the foot of the Hude, Middleton-in-Teesdale. From the left, Harry Richardson, Sidney Bowron and ...... Eccles.

steel driving wheels, which not only had little grip on the hills, but often got bogged on the softer stretches of the road, the attempt had to be abandoned.[6] However, in 1915 there was another attempt to overcome the problem and become more efficient. There was erected at Langdon Beck, a short distance along the road to Valance Lodge, a large storage hopper into which the horse drawn carts could tip the loads brought down from the mines. It was then possible to employ steam wagons to convey the barytes to Middleton. The wagons were an interesting variety, all on steel tyres, with the exception of the last to be employed which was a Foden on solid rubber tyres (see photographs).

Then in 1918 there was a further revision in the transport arrangements which did away with the use of horses and carts, with the exception of those engaged on site work.

There was laid from Low Level a narrow gauge railway direct to Cow Rake which, in addition to being used for washing and dressing, became the collecting point for all the mines. For it was from there that there was erected an overhead ropeway driven by a gas engine, on which was hung kibbles which conveyed the barytes to two storage hoppers erected by the roadside a short distance below the present No. 1 Wrentnall Cottages, and then to the station by steam wagon.

However, for a number of reasons which included a drop in demand, and having to face a charge of pollution at their works which were situated at Jarrow Slake on the Tyne, the company was forced into liquidation in 1922. The liquidators and receivers being Messrs Price Waterhouse and Co., 31 Mosley Street, Newcastle upon Tyne.

References

1. Report dated 16 October 1874 which was commissioned by the directors of the Dubby Sike Company who were forming a limited company to take over the Dubby Sike mining sett.

2. Robinson's name appears a number of times indicating the position he held in the different companies, most of which he helped to form during the second half of the nineteenth century.

3. Teesdale Mercury dated December 1892.

4. See also plan of mining setts.

5. Teesdale Mercury dated 10 December 1902.

6. My father who was one of the crew of two who manned the wagon.

Notes

1. I acknowledge the use of *The Mineral Statistics of Yorkshire, Durham and Northumberland* published by The Department of Economic History, University of Exeter, in association with The Northern Mine Research Society and The Peak District Mines Historical Society.

2. New Road and Toll House. 'This road leads, in about two miles or less, up to Cowgreen Mine and Toll House...' states James Backhouse in *Upper Teesdale Past and Present* p. 30 (1898). The last occupiers of the house were Mr and Mrs Harry Heward.

3. The Oil Engine was not a diesel compression-ignition oil engine, but one which ran on vaporised paraffin. A description of the engine appears in the *Oil Engine Manual* published by The Temple Press Limited.

List of subscribers

J K Almond, Eston.
John M Almond, Warkworth.
P J Andrews, Basingstoke.
Mr K Archer, Consett.
Robert W Atkinson, Stanley.
Doreen & Bill Attwood, Gateshead.
Roger Bade.
Tina Bailey, Newhouse.
Stewart & Jane Beaty, Catton.
Rob Benton, Basingstoke.
Frank Bouweraerts, Wearhead.
Peter & Jean Bowes, Stanhope.
David Bridges, Laceby.
Trevor & Shelagh Bridges, Ovington.
John & Lena Burgess, Durham City.
A J Cairns.
Helen Cannam, Harperley.
Mr Edward Carrington, Hexham.
Bryan & Dorothy Chambers, Durham.
Simon Chapman, Brotton.
Alan F Clapham, Lincoln.
Mr & Mrs A Clarkson, Burnopfield.
Ian & Kathryn Cornwall, Patrington.
B & J Corrigan, Whickham.
J L Crosby, Stanhope.
Sally Crowther, East Loftus.
Janet & Ken Dawson, Frosterley.
Dr Ian W Drummond, Manchester.
Sir Kingsley Dunham, Elvet.
Dr J R Elliott, Newcastle upon Tyne.
Denise Fisher.
Ian Forbes, Westgate.
Pam Forbes, Westgate.
Mr J R Foster-Smith, Middleton-in-Teesdale.
Ken & Audrey Gardiner, Lanchester.
Kate Garratt, Alston.
Dr F L Gilbert.
Michael Gill, Sutton-in-Craven
William & Louisa Gordon, South Moor.
John Gosden, Durham City.
Dick & Margaret Graham, Rowlands Gill.
Dr Martin Green, Durham.
Bill & Marjorie Grigg, East Blackdene.
The Grigg family, Perth.
Joan & Derek Groom, Lanehead.
E T & J M Hancock, High Shincliffe.

Roger & Patience Healey, Romsey.
J M Helliwell, Retford.
Dave Holroyde, Durham.
R Ireland, Leyland.
Mrs M M Jackson, Scarisbrick.
Peter Jackson, Billingham.
The Jackson family, Newcastle.
Harry James, Gosforth.
Jackie & Michael Jones, Durham.
I M Jowett, Stanhope.
Ian C Kerr, Strathaven.
David Kidd, South Shields.
Peter Lanham, Nenthead.
Brian & Helen Lawrenson, Catton
Lucas family, Sawley.
Mike & Mavis Luff, Ravenstone.
Duncan & Sylvia MacCallum, Nunthorpe.
Hilda & John MacPherson, Middlesbrough.
Gerry & Carol Madden, Milton Keynes.
Alec & Margaret Manchester, Sunniside.
Cliff & Dorothy McCarthy, St John's Chapel.
Nathen & Ian McVittie, Penrith.
Mr & Mrs P Nattrass, Westgate.
North Pennine Heritage Trust.
Mr & Mrs M Ould, Garrigill
N G Pace, Lerici, Italy.
Gordon Parkin, Wolsingham.
Russ Parkin, Wolsingham.
R Peel, Newcastle.
Dick Phillips & Nan Simmons, Nenthead.
G A Pickin, Guisborough.
Mr W K Pirt, Worksop.
Miss E M Simpson, Pickering.
Mr & Mrs A Smethurst, Penrith.
Mark & Linda Smith, Thorpe Thewles
John Stott, Bolton.
Carol Sutton, Nenthead.
Charles & Peggy Tanner, Knutsford.
J S Thomas, Durham.
Roland & Audrey Thomas, Woking
Alan & Julia Thorogood, Virginia Water.
D J Tyerman, Bishop's Stortford.
Gordon & Susan Whitfield, Allendale.
Peter Wilkinson, Frosterley
Malcolm, Debra, Emma & Sarah Woodward,
Newcastle upon Tyne.